MULTIPLE-CHOICE AND FREE-RESPONSE QUESTIONS IN PREPARATION FOR THE AP STATISTICS EXAMINATION

(THIRD EDITION)

By

Michael Allwood
Brunswick School
Greenwich, CT

D&S MARKETING SYSTEMS, INC.
1205 38th Street Brooklyn, NY 11218

w w w . d s m a r k e t i n g . c o m

ISBN # 978-1-934780-16-9 / 1-934780-16-2

PREFACE

Welcome to the third edition of *Multiple-Choice & Free-Response Questions in Preparation for the AP Statistics Examination*!

This book provides help and support for students as they prepare for the Advanced Placement exam. The first section, "Top Tips for AP Statistics," gives important advice both on a general and a content-specific level. This is followed by "Using the TI-Nspire on the AP Statistics Examination," by Heather Overstreet, where important advice and guidance are provided for students using the TI-Nspire calculator. The third section, "Summary Exercises," provides comprehensive questions in five of the major topic areas, comprising about half of the AP Statistics course content. These sections are followed by five sample exams, each of which has the same format as the actual AP exam: 40 multiple-choice questions and 6 free-response questions. In each case, as on the AP exam, the sixth free-response question (known as the investigative task) is designed to include ideas a little beyond those encountered during the AP Statistics course.

I strongly recommend – to students and teachers alike – a detailed reading of the Top Tips, as valuable points can be gained on the exam by following the suggestions made there. Additionally, by tackling the Summary Exercises, referring to class notes and a textbook as necessary and applying the ideas learned in the Top Tips, the student can build a virtually comprehensive knowledge in the topics that are covered in that section. The practice exams can then be taken either as further review using a textbook and class notes, or under conditions similar to those of the actual test.

In each exam (as in the AP), Section I (multiple-choice) should be completed in 90 minutes, as should Section II (free-response). In Section II, students are advised to spend 65 minutes on the first five free-response questions (Part A) and 25 minutes on the investigative task (Part B). Workspace has been provided for each question, and the tables and formulas that are included on the AP Statistics exam are provided in the last section of the book.

I would like to thank my wife, Anne, for her support and encouragement during the creation of this book. I am also very grateful to my editor, Daren Starnes, whose advice and expertise I greatly appreciate, and to Tammi Pruzansky of D&S Marketing Systems, Inc., who typeset the book and prepared the final copy for printing.

All communications concerning this book should be addressed to:

D&S Marketing Systems, Inc.
1205 38th Street
Brooklyn, NY 11218
www.dsmarketing.com

TABLE OF CONTENTS

Top Tips for AP Statistics

PART I: INTRODUCTION AND GENERAL ADVICE

Introduction

Welcome!

Success on the AP Statistics exam depends on two very important factors. First, you need a good knowledge and understanding of the material in the course. Second, you need to know what is expected of you on the exam: there are particular approaches that are required, and if you're not familiar with these approaches, you are liable to lose a significant number of points.

It is this second factor that we address in the Top Tips. For each section of the syllabus we will look at exactly what you need to do, basing the advice on many years' grading of the exam. And, of course, the idea is that your understanding of the material will be advanced in the process.

Having started with a review of the format of the exam and some advice as to how to approach the two sections, we will proceed with the topics on the syllabus, for each providing a list of the knowledge and skills needed, and following that with the Top Tips.

The Format of the Exam

The AP Statistics exam has two sections: 1½ hours of multiple-choice (40 questions) and 1½ hours of free-response (6 questions), and the two sections are equally weighted. In the multiple-choice section you will receive 1 point for every correct answer and zero for any answer left blank. (There is no longer any penalty for guessing on the multiple-choice section. So, if you are unsure as to the answer to a question, it's in your interest to make a guess.) In the free-response section, the first five questions are designed to take 13 minutes each, and Question 6 should take around 25 minutes. Question 6 will account for 25% of your free-response grade.

There is a break between the two sections of the exam, and calculators are allowed on both sections.

How to do Well on the Multiple-Choice Section, and on Multiple-Choice Questions in General

You should be aware that multiple-choice questions are liable to confuse you, particularly when you work on them during the course or in the run-up to the exam. Imagine yourself at some point during the year: you have a good but insecure understanding of a topic. You then attempt a multiple-choice question. All of the wrong answers are designed to tempt you – they have that element of plausibility, and so they lead you to doubt the correct understanding that you previously had. And the danger is that this element of doubt will linger on at the back of your mind, even after you have checked your answers and supposedly reaffirmed your understanding.

So here's what you should do:

- *Do not attempt a multiple-choice question until you know that you have a strong understanding of the relevant material*

  The first multiple-choice questions that you come across on any given topic might in fact be on the test you do in class on that topic. So you need to be really sure that you understand the material fully before you take the test – and you can do this by reviewing the material thoroughly, and, if possible, by finding an opportunity to explain it to a friend. You will find that putting the ideas into words greatly increases the robustness of your understanding – and no doubt you'll help the friend, too.

- *Stop before you look at the possible answers*

  This applies to all multiple-choice questions you do, including those on the exam itself. Once you have read the question (not the possible answers), *mentally pause*. Reaffirm your own understanding and decide what you believe the answer to be, *before you look at the answers*. You might just have to glance at the answers to get an idea of the *kind* of thing that is being asked for, but make sure throughout the process that *your* thinking is dominant – your *correct* thinking, as opposed to the bogus thinking of the incorrect answers.

  You will find in the pages that follow many multiple-choice questions, all of the style and level that you are likely to encounter on the AP Statistics exam. Some of them are straightforward, and some possibly challenging. You can use them all for practice of the steps given here, and to re-affirm the strong understanding of statistics that you have built up during the course. Do well!

Guidance for the Free-Response Section

Since the exam was first given in 1997, the readers have seen, over and over again, particular mistakes that students make in their approach and in their answering of the questions. Here's how to avoid those mistakes:

- *Use your time wisely*

  As mentioned above, Question 6 will count for 25% of your free-response grade, so it's important that you restrict yourself to 13 minutes for each of Questions 1-5, thereby leaving yourself with the 25 minutes that you need for Question 6. Some teachers tell their students to start with Question 1, then do Question 6, and then complete the remaining questions.

- *Write answers that are clear, succinct, and complete*

  Read the question carefully, decide what you need to say, and say just that. If you write long rambling answers, you are probably wasting valuable time and you are in danger of writing something incorrect and therefore losing credit. (And don't feel that you have to fill the space provided for your answer.)

- *Always answer in the context of the question*

  For example, if the question is about plants and fertilizer, your answers must refer to plants and fertilizer.

- *Always show your work*

  Some students find this hard to believe, but in AP Statistics, a numerical answer with no work shown, or a written statement with no explanation, will receive *no credit*.

- *Give just one answer to the question*

  If you give two or more solutions or explanations, then you will be graded on the least correct of your answers. So it's up to you to decide which answer to submit. Cross out the other solution with a pencil – you can always erase your crossing out if you change your mind later.

- *Include all the steps of your argument*

  For example, one question described a phone survey that is designed to estimate the proportion of an adult population that does not have a high school diploma. Students were asked to state one form of bias and to describe its effect on the result of the survey. Many students pointed out that phone surveys ignore people who have no phone, and people without phones will often not have high school diplomas. But the students failed to go on to say that this would result in an *underestimate* of the proportion of the population who do not have a high school diploma. It may seem obvious, but you have to say it.

- *When making a comparison, be sure to include consideration of both of the items that are being compared*

  Suppose, for example, you are explaining that in a particular situation a Type II error is more serious than a Type I error. Then it's important that you describe the seriousness of a Type II error *and* explain why a Type I error is *less* serious.

- *Naming is not enough for description*

  For example, if you are asked to describe a bias involved in a survey, and your response is "response bias," then you have only *named* the bias, not *described* it. Credit would only be given to students who explain what is happening and what effect it might have on the survey.

- *Interpreting the value includes <u>giving</u> the value*

  Let's say you are given a computer display and you are asked to interpret the value of the correlation, r. Then you need to include the *value* of r in your answer.

- *When drawing a graph, make sure that you include labels and scales*

Label every axis and scale every axis. And, very importantly, if you're using a comparative display, such as a back-to-back stemplot or parallel boxplots, then make sure that you show which part of the diagram refers to which of the groups that are being compared.

- *If you can't do one part of a question, don't assume that you will be unable to do the rest of the question.*

- *If you need the answer to an earlier part of the question, and you were unable to do that part, make up a feasible answer*

An incorrect answer to, for example, part (a), correctly used in part (b), will gain full credit for part (b). So if you couldn't do part (a), make up a feasible answer and use it in part (b).

- *Be prepared for Question 6 to involve ideas that you haven't covered in class*

This is the idea of Question 6 – to have you think for yourself in a new situation. So keep calm, and set about doing what the question asks you to do – you have been thinking statistically for almost a year, and so the ideas are very unlikely to be beyond you.

General Guidance

- *Know the material*

This is possibly stating the obvious, but there's no replacement for a full knowledge and understanding of the material that has been covered in the course. Be aware, in particular, that the multiple-choice questions can test you on any detail that you have encountered.

- *Retain your intelligence!*

A question might at first seem to be different from anything that you have encountered during the year, but if you have paid attention during the course there will be very little in the exam that is truly beyond your understanding. And everything in statistics is logical – so if you retain your common sense and explain your thoughts, you will probably get the question right. (A few good nights' sleep before the exam will help with this!)

PART II: THE TOPICS

1. *Graphical and Numerical Methods for Describing Data*

You will need to be able to construct the following types of displays and draw conclusions from them:

- □ bar chart
- □ dotplot
- □ stemplot
- □ boxplot
- □ histogram

You will need to be able to draw conclusions from a

- □ cumulative (relative) frequency curve

For a given set of data, you should be able calculate and draw conclusions from the

- □ median
- □ quartiles
- □ percentiles
- □ interquartile range
- □ range
- □ mean
- □ variance
- □ standard deviation
- □ … and all of the above when the data are given in the form of a frequency distribution

You should also be able to:

- □ describe shapes of distributions, including positive and negative (right and left) skewness
- □ decide by doing calculations which value(s) is/are outliers
- □ comment on the appropriateness of the use of measures such as the mean and the standard deviation for particular sets of data
- □ know the effect of positive (or negative) skewness on the relationship between the mean and the median
- □ calculate the new values of measures such as the mean, median, standard deviation, etc., after the original dataset has been transformed by addition/subtraction and/or multiplication/division
- □ calculate z-scores and use them to compare the positions of particular scores within their respective distributions

Top Tips

- *Know how to describe shapes of distributions*

If you believe that a distribution is roughly symmetrical, then that is exactly the phrase to use: "roughly symmetrical." Never say "normal," as we can never be that precise, and do not say "evenly distributed," as that could be taken to mean something else. In some circumstances, "approximately normal" is accepted, but even this is dangerous, since in the case of boxplots it is not possible to say that a distribution that is roughly symmetrical will in fact be shaped like a normal distribution. So "roughly symmetrical" is the phrase to use!

- *Know how to compare distributions*

Having been given a comparative display, such as a back-to-back stemplot or parallel boxplots, you are very often asked to compare the distributions. In this situation you are expected to make your comparison in terms of <u>center</u>, <u>spread</u>, and <u>shape</u>, and you have to use phrases that actually compare – such as "is greater than" or "is less than." Saying, for example, "The median for the boys is 71 inches while the median for the girls is 66.5 inches" is not enough, since you haven't pointed out that 71 is bigger than 66.5. Here's a model answer from a student who has been asked to compare a set of boys' heights to a set of girls' heights:

> The center of the distribution for the boys (around 71 inches) is greater than the center of the distribution for the girls (around 67 inches).
>
> The range for the boys (8 inches) is greater than the range for the girls (6 inches).
>
> The distribution of the boys' heights is positively skewed. The distribution of the girls' heights is roughly symmetrical.

Notice that you are not required to use actual measures, such as medians, but if you choose to use them, and do so correctly, that will be accepted.

- *In graphs, make sure that you use proper labeling*

As mentioned in the guidance for the free-response section, when you draw a graph, make sure that your axes are scaled and labeled. And, very importantly, when you are drawing a comparative display such as a back-to-back stemplot or parallel boxplots, be sure to label which part of the diagram refers to which of the groups that are being compared.

- *Use the phrase "Middle 50%"*

If you are looking at a boxplot of, for example, girls' heights, and you want to refer to the box in the middle of the graph, the phrase to use is "the middle 50% of the girls' heights." Remember that the *interquartile range* is something else – it's the result you get when you subtract the lower (first) quartile from the upper (third) quartile.

- *Know how to interpret the standard deviation*

Let's suppose you know that the standard deviation of the girls' heights is 2.83 inches, and you are asked to interpret this value. Here's a model answer:

2.83 inches is a typical deviation of a girl's height from the mean height of the girls.

Notice that our model student gives the answer in context!

- *Only use the empirical rule in the case of a normal distribution*

The empirical rule states that in a normal distribution, approximately 68% of the observations fall within one standard deviation of the mean, approximately 95% of the observations fall within two standard deviations of the mean, and approximately 99.7% of the observations fall within three standard deviations of the mean. Many students make the mistake of using the empirical rule when it is not known that the distribution is normal. So keep away from the empirical rule unless you are certain that you are dealing with a quantity that is normally distributed, and even then it is advisable to preface your remarks by saying, "We know that the distribution is approximately normal, and so…"

- *Remember that there is no merit in skewness*

Suppose we know that the distribution of salaries paid by a company is positively skewed. This means that the spread of the salaries above the center of the distribution is greater than the spread of the salaries below the center of the distribution. It doesn't tell us anything about whether this company is paying high salaries or low salaries.

2. *Correlation and Regression*

<u>Correlation, and Linear Regression</u>

You should be able to:

- ☐ draw a scatterplot
- ☐ use a scatterplot to describe the closeness to a linear relationship
- ☐ use a scatterplot to describe the direction of a relationship (positive or negative)
- ☐ determine the value of the correlation, r, and the equation of the least squares regression line from computer output
- ☐ interpret the value of the correlation
- ☐ interpret the slope of the regression line
- ☐ decide whether the y-intercept of the regression line has a meaningful interpretation and, if so, give this interpretation
- ☐ use the regression line to estimate a value
- ☐ explain the inappropriateness of extrapolation
- ☐ explain that the value of the correlation is unaffected by adding a constant to all of the x-values (or y-values) and by multiplying all the x-values (or y-values) by a constant
- ☐ interpret the value of r^2
- ☐ calculate residuals or use residuals to calculate actual values

☐ draw a residual plot

☐ use a residual plot to establish the appropriateness (or not) of a linear model

Nonlinear Regression

You should:

☐ understand that transforming the variables can produce a linear fit

☐ be able to determine the appropriateness of a linear model using a residual plot

☐ be able to translate the linear fit of the transformed variables into the nonlinear fit of the original variables

☐ know that a linear fit for log y against x implies an exponential realationship between y and x, and a linear fit for log y against log x implies a power relationship between y and x.

 Top Tips

• *Know how to interpret the correlation, r*

For this you are expected to address the *strength*, *direction*, and *linearity* of the relationship, *in context*. So here's a model answer:

> ✎ $r = 0.769$. There is a moderately strong, positive, linear relationship between the height of the plant and the amount of fertilizer used.

Students in class often ask how large r needs to be in order for the relationship to be classified as "strong," "moderately strong," or "weak." This is not straightforward to answer as it depends on the size of the sample and, to some extent, the context. Consequently, the readers of the exam are relatively lenient on this point. Just make a decision, and your answer will probably be accepted.

• *Know how to interpret the slope of the regression line*

Let's suppose that the regression line relating running speed in mph (x) and pulse rate in beats per minute (y) has equation $\hat{y} = 62.143 + 15.953x$, and you are asked to interpret the slope of the regression line. Here's a model answer:

> ✎ For each one mile per hour increase in running speed, the <u>predicted</u> pulse rate increases by 15.953 beats per minute.

The word "predicted" could be replaced by "expected," or you could say that the pulse rate increases by "approximately" 15.953 beats per minute. Whatever your choice, you have to include a word that indicates that it's not the *actual* pulse rates that increase according to the given equation.

Likewise, if you were interpreting the y-intercept, you would need to say that it is the *predicted* pulse rate when the running speed is zero.

• *When giving the equation of the regression line, define x and $\hat{y}$*

Let's suppose that you've been given a computer display that includes the slope and the *y*-intercept in the example above, and that you've been asked to state the equation of the regression line. Then it is not enough just to say "$\hat{y} = 62.143 + 15.953x$." You have to state that *x* is the running speed and $\hat{y}$ is the predicted pulse rate.

Alternatively, you can state the equation in words:
Predicted pulse rate $= 62.143 + 15.953$ (speed).

• *Know and understand the interpretation of r^2*

Let's suppose that a boy's running speed is calculated on each of his birthdays. A scatterplot is constructed, plotting speed against age, and the value of r^2 is found to be 0.751. Here's a model interpretation of this value of r^2:

> ✎ 75.1% of the variation in running speed is explained by the least-squares regression line relating speed and age.

Many students decide that this is very complicated, and resort to memorizing the interpretation (with varying degrees of success). However, the concepts involved are not really all that complex, so we will spend a short time now getting to grips with the relevant ideas.

So let's return to the example of the boy and his running speed, and let's assume that his running speed has a precise linear relationship with his age. The scatterplot will look like this:

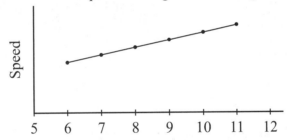

The boy's running speeds are not all the same, so there is some variation in running speed. All of this variation in running speed is explained by the fact that the boy is getting older and that his speed is related to his age by the straight line.

But, even if basically the boy's speed is linearly related to his age, there will be variations *from* the line due to various factors on his birthdays (what he has eaten, how tired he is, etc.). So the scatterplot is more likely to look like this:

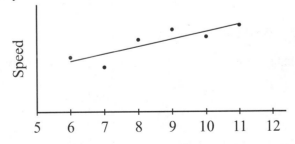

Given that the line has remained unchanged, there will now be *more* variation in the boy's speeds. (Either this makes intuitive sense to you, or you will have to accept this fact.) Some of that variation is explained by the fact that the boy is getting older and that his speed is related to his age by the straight line, and the rest is explained by the fact that the points are not exactly on the line. The proportion of the variability in speed that *is* explained by the straight line relationship is r^2.

3. *Observational Studies and Experiments*

You will need to:

☐ know what distinguishes an experiment from an observational study

Observational Studies

You will need to:

☐ understand why causation cannot be inferred from an observational study

☐ know what is meant by a census, and when it would be used

☐ know the definition of a simple random sample (SRS) and know how an SRS would be obtained

You should know how the following sampling methods would be implemented and why they would be used:

☐ stratified random sampling

☐ cluster sampling

☐ convenience sampling

You should be aware of the need to avoid, and be able to delineate the effect of, the forms of bias known as:

☐ undercoverage (selection) bias

☐ nonresponse bias

☐ response bias

Experimental design

You should know and understand the vocabulary of

☐ explanatory variables (factors) and response variables, levels of explanatory variables, and treatments

You should know:

☐ how and why to randomize the assignment of experimental subjects to the groups

☐ why there is need for a control group

□ how and why to use a placebo

□ single blinding: what it is, when it is possible, why it is used, and how it is achieved

□ double blinding: what it is, when it is possible, why it is used, and how it is achieved

□ blocking: why block, according to what variable, and how

□ how to make a matched pairs design, and why this is advantageous

□ the meaning of replication, and why it is needed

□ to what extent the result of an experiment can be generalized to the whole population

Top Tips

• *Confounding variables*

Suppose that an observational study has revealed that people who exercise regularly tend to have lower blood pressure than people who do not, and you are asked to explain, giving an example of a possible confounding variable, why this does not mean that regular exercise causes low blood pressure. Here's a model answer:

> It may well be that people who exercise regularly tend to eat healthy food, and people who do not exercise regularly tend not to eat healthy food. In which case, it could be the healthy food that is causing the low blood pressure, not the exercise.

The link between exercise and healthy food, provided here by the phrase "tend to be the sort of people who…" is all-important. Students who say, "There are other factors, such as healthy food, that promote low blood pressure" are not addressing this link, and are therefore not explaining how the study could have turned out in the way that it did without regular exercise causing low blood pressure.

• *Remember that sample size is rarely the problem*

If you are asked to describe a problem in the design of an observational study, the sample size being too small is very unlikely to be the correct answer. The reason for this is that the mathematics that would be used to analyze the result would take account of the sample size. More likely, you should be looking for a source of *bias* (see the next tip).

• *Know how to describe bias*

Let's suppose that you are given the design of an observational study and you are asked to describe some form of bias that might be involved. You will need to explain that the issue you delineate is likely to make the result of the study inaccurate in *one direction*, and you should state *which* direction (up or down) it is likely to push the result.

For example, suppose a student wishes to estimate the mean amount of sleep for students at her school. She asks every fifth student entering the school, up to the time that the school day starts. The fact that she misses the students who are late to school is a source of bias since those who are late are likely to have had less sleep on average, and so the survey is likely to *over*estimate the mean amount of sleep. Without the likely effect on the survey, you have not described why this undercoverage is a source of bias.

- *Don't talk about sampling in the context of experiments*

Experiments are usually done with volunteers (if the experimental units are people) and very rarely with a random sample from the population being considered. What happens in experiments is *random assignment* to the groups.

- *Know how to describe the need for a control group*

Let's suppose that an experiment to test the effectiveness of a new drug for reducing blood pressure is being described, and you are asked to explain why a control group is needed. Here's a model answer:

 If you didn't have a control group and the subjects' blood pressures were on average significantly reduced, then you wouldn't know whether this reduction had come about as a result of the drug or as a result of some external factor such as an increase in sunshine. If, however, you have a group that is <u>not</u> given the drug, and this group does <u>not</u> on average experience a decrease in blood pressure, then we might be able to conclude that the drug is effective.

Two things about this external factor: First, it should not be referred to as a confounding variable, as it will affect *all* of the subjects – in other words there isn't a link with *one* of the groups. Second, it should be something that could feasibly affect all the subjects – it's no good saying, for example, that the subjects might be getting more sleep, unless you think there's something in the design of the experiment that will encourage all of the subjects to get more sleep.

- *Be very careful how you use the phrase "confounding variable"*

Think back to the first tip in this section, and note once more that for a variable to be a confounding variable, its values must differ systematically between the groups in the study. The eating of healthy food (or not) was acceptable as a confounding variable because it was suggested that those who exercise tend to eat healthy food and those who do *not* exercise tend *not* to eat healthy food. When you're answering a question, unless you're absolutely sure that the variable you're talking about differs between the groups in the study, it's best to avoid saying "confounding variable," and use, instead, a phrase such as "another variable that might affect the subjects' blood pressures" (or whatever the response variable happens to be).

- *Know how to achieve random assignment*

For example, suppose the question concerns an experiment that uses 50 volunteers, and you have to describe how to randomly assign them to two groups of 25 – a treatment group and a control group. Here's a model solution:

Put the names of the 50 volunteers on pieces of paper and put the pieces of paper in a hat. Mix the pieces of paper, and then pick names from the hat at random. The first 25 names picked will go into the treatment group, and the remaining people will go into the control group.

This "hat method" will always work, so it's a good idea to use this approach, unless some other method is specified. There are two things to be careful about with this method. First, make sure that you include the instruction to mix the names and/or to pick them at random from the hat. Second, be sure to specify *which* group the first 25 (or whatever) names go into. Just saying "one of the groups" is not enough.

There's another method that students often use which does *not* constitute complete randomization: "Take a list of the volunteers and flip a coin for each volunteer. If the coin comes up heads, the volunteer goes into the treatment group, and if it's tails the volunteer goes into the control group. Once you have a group of 25, put the remaining volunteers into the other group." This doesn't constitute complete randomization as, for example, the last two people on the list are very likely to end up in the same group.

- *If you are asked for a "completely randomized design," this means that you should not include blocking*

- *Be careful not to say that randomization or blocking will "eliminate" differences between the groups*

Randomization (random assignment) ensures that any differences between the groups occur through bad luck only. It doesn't *eliminate* differences between the groups.

Blocking, by age for example, will ensure that the groups are *very similar* in terms of age, but it will not *eliminate* age differences between the groups.

- *Give complete answers to questions about blinding*

Let's suppose that a question cites an experiment to evaluate a treatment for clothing fabric, the treatment being designed to help people who suffer from skin inflammation. You are told in the stem of the question that the treatment leaves the fabric unchanged in appearance, and you are asked in one part of the question to state whether the experiment could be conducted in a double blind manner.

Now "double blind" means first that the participants do not know whether they are being given the treated or the untreated material, and second that the people who measure the response variable (the effect of the material on the skin) do not know who received the treated or the untreated material.

For the first criterion, it is necessary that you state in your answer that *we are told that the treatment leaves the fabric unchanged in appearance*, and so therefore that it is possible for the participants not to know which group they're in.

For the second criterion, be sure that you state that *the people who measure the effect of the fabric on the skin* do not know who received the treated or the untreated material. Just to say that the "experimenters" don't know is not enough.

• *Understand the rationale for – and the implementation of – blocking*

Let's suppose that an experiment is being designed to compare two treatments to prevent hair loss in men. We will look now at why and how blocking might be used in this context.

Why do we need blocking? Suppose that we believe that *older men will react less well than younger men* to these treatments. We therefore want our treatment groups to be as close as possible in terms of age, so that if we find a difference between the two groups in terms of their reactions to the treatments, we then know that this difference is unlikely to have anything to do with any age differences between the two groups. This is achieved by blocking by age.

Blocking is implemented as follows: First, the participants are split into *blocks* according to their age (for example, a block consisting of the two oldest men, a block consisting of the next two oldest men, and so on). Second the *treatments* are assigned randomly within each block (so, to continue the example, you flip a coin to find out which of the two oldest men gets treatment A and which gets treatment B, and so on for the other blocks). It is clear then that the two treatment groups (the group of subjects who are given treatment A and the group of subjects who are given treatment B) are very similar in terms of age.

It's important to remember that blocks consist of *similar* experimental units.

4. Probability and Simulation

You should understand and be proficient with the following:

☐ Venn diagrams and the "addition rule": $P(A \cup B) = P(A) + P(B) - P(A \cap B)$

☐ mutually exclusive events

☐ conditional probability

☐ probability and conditional probability from tables of frequencies

☐ independent events: are given events independent?

☐ use of $P(A \cap B) = P(A) \cdot P(B)$ for independent events

☐ use of tree diagrams

☐ reverse conditional probabilities (sometimes referred to as "Bayes' Rule")

☐ "without replacement" problems (e.g., when selecting four vehicles at random without replacement from a set of 10 sedans and 5 SUVs, what is the probability that they are all sedans?)

☐ use of a table of random digits to simulate probabilities such as 0.3, 5/9, 0.47

✎ Top Tips

• *Understand mutually exclusive and independent events*

Keep the two ideas separate in your mind.

Two events are **mutually exclusive** if they can't both happen at the same time. For example, suppose we have a set of 40 cards consisting of 10 red cards (numbered 1–10), 10 blue cards (numbered 1–10), 10 green cards (numbered 1–10), and 10 purple cards (numbered 1–10). We will we pick one card at random. Let A be the event that the card is red and let B be the event that the card is green. Then the events A and B are mutually exclusive, since the card that we pick can't be both blue and green. Notice that if two events A and B are mutually exclusive, then $P(A \cap B) = 0$. The meaning of "mutually exclusive" is easy to remember because of the word "exclusive." The events *exclude* each other in the sense that if one of the events is happening, the other one can't be happening.

Two events are **independent** if they don't affect each other – that's what the word *independent* means. The easiest way to think of this is when we're doing two things that clearly have no effect on each other, such as flipping a coin and rolling a cube with faxes numbered 1 through 6. If A is that event that the coin shows a head and B is the event that the cube shows a six, then clearly the probability that B happens is unaffected by whether or not A has happened. To look at this another way, we're saying that $P(B \mid A)$ and $P(B)$ are the same.

But we need also to be aware of the possibility of independence when just *one* thing is happening. Let's return to the set of 40 cards mentioned above. Picking one card at rondom, let A be the event that the card is purple and let B be the event that the card is an 8. Then $P(B) = 4/40 = 1/10$ and $P(B \mid A) = 1/10$. Knowing that A is happening makes no difference to the probability that B is happening. So these two events A and B are independent also.

Suppose, on the other hand, that A is the event that the number on the card is greater than 7, and B is the event that the number on the card is an 8. Then $P(B) = 4/40 = 1/10$ and $P(B \mid A) = 4/12 = 1/3$. Knowing that A is happening changes the probability that B is happening. So, in this case, the events A and B are *not* independent.

Independence can be checked in many different ways. Any one of the statements, $P(B \mid A) = P(B)$, $P(A \mid B) = P(A)$, and $P(A \mid B) = P(A \mid B^c)$, is sufficient to prove independence, as is any statement that demonstrates that one event happening or not happening does not affect the probability that the other is happening. The statement that $P(A \cap B) = P(A) \cdot P(B)$ is also sufficient for proving that the events A and B are independent.

- *Understand the relationship between mutually exclusive and independent events*

  Having told you to keep the two ideas separate in your mind (which you should definitely do until you are confident with them), we are now going to relate the two.

  If two events are mutually exclusive, then knowing that one of them is happening means that the other *can't* be happening. So the events very much do affect each other, meaning that they are *not* independent.

  Now looking at this relationship the other way around, if two events A and B are independent, then $P(A \cap B) = P(A) \cdot P(B)$, and so, unless one of $P(A)$ or $P(B)$ is zero, $P(A \cap B)$ can't be zero, and so A and B are not mutually exclusive.

- *When you are asked to describe a simulation process, be sure to give all the steps*

You need to include: where in the random digit table you will start, in what direction you will move, how many digits at a time you will use, what sets of digits are assigned to what outcome (including, possibly, some to be ignored), to ignore repeats (if applicable), what governs when the run of the simulation will stop, and what needs to be written down (e.g. the total score or the mean score) once the run of the simulation is finished.

- *When you are asked to carry out a simulation process, be sure to give the summary information that is required*

A question could ask you to perform five runs of your simulation, and to note the mean score for each run. Be sure that you actually carry out the second part of the instruction!

5. *Random Variables*

You should be familiar with the following:

- ☐ distinguishing between discrete and continuous random variables
- ☐ forming a probability distribution from given information
- ☐ representing a probability distribution in graph form
- ☐ finding the mean, variance, and standard deviation of a random variable from its probability distribution
- ☐ calculating probabilities from a probability density function using areas (for continuous random variables)
- ☐ recognizing that a random variable is binomially distributed, and calculating probabilities
- ☐ the formulas for the mean and standard deviation of a binomially distributed random variable
- ☐ recognizing that a random variable is geometrically distributed, and calculating probabilities
- ☐ problems using the normal distribution

You should also know the following:

- ☐ If $Y = aX + b$, where a and b are constants, then $E(Y) = aE(X) + b$ and $\mathrm{Var}(Y) = a^2 \mathrm{Var}(X)$ (and so that $\sigma_Y = |a|\sigma_X$)
- ☐ $E(X + Y) = E(X) + E(Y)$ and, if X and Y are independent, that $\mathrm{Var}(X + Y) = \mathrm{Var}(X) + \mathrm{Var}(Y)$ (and consequently that $\sigma_{aX+bY} = \sqrt{a^2\sigma_X^2 + b^2\sigma_Y^2}$)
- ☐ $\mathrm{Var}(X - Y) = \mathrm{Var}(X) + \mathrm{Var}(Y)$
- ☐ If the random variables X and Y are independent and normally distributed, and a, b are constants (positive or negative), then $aX + bY$ is normally distributed. (Note that since b can be negative, this includes *subtraction* of multiples of independent normally distributed random variables.)

Top Tips

The fields of probability and random variables are the most numerical in the course, and so the free-response questions on these topics have often been the ones that are most successfully answered by students. The most common sources of error, apart from not knowing the material, tend to involve not showing adequate work – and this is what we will concern ourselves with in the tips for this section.

- *If you are asked to find the mean and/or the standard deviation (or variance) of a random variable using its probability distribution, use the formulas and write out the calculations*

  It is possible to find the mean and the standard deviation of a discrete random variable using a calculator. However, if you use this method, it is very difficult to show your work in such a way that will get you full credit. The best approach, therefore, is to use the formulas and write out your calculations, and then you can always check your answers using the calculator if you have time.

- *Any time you use your calculator, show your work in some way that doesn't use calculator notation*

  If, for example, you are dealing with the normal distribution, draw the normal curve and add to it the relevant information. If you are finding a probability derived from the binomial distribution, either show the formula with the numbers plugged in, or, if you are using one of the calculator functions, state in words or in mathematical notation (not calculator notation!) the fact that the relevant quantity is binomially distributed, the value of n, the value of p, and what it is you are finding the probability of. To generalize, you need to show, in mathematical notation or in words, all the quantities you use in your calculation.

- *In questions involving standard distributions such as binomial, geometric, and normal distributions, be sure to state the distribution and the parameters as well as providing a calculation*

  For example, suppose that a question states that a cube with faces numbered 1 through 6 will be rolled 8 times, and asks for the probability that 3 or fewer sixes will result. The numerical answer to this question can be obtained directly with a calculator (using binomcdf(8,1/6,3), for example). However, in order to receive full credit you need to state that the distribution of the number of sixes is binomial and that the parameters are $n = 8$ and $p = 1/6$, as well providing a calculation of the numerical answer to the question.

6. Sampling Distributions

You should:

- ☐ know the language and notation of population parameters and sample statistics
- ☐ be able to compare two statistics according to their lack of bias and their low variability
- ☐ know that the sampling distribution of the sample mean, $\overline{x}$, has mean μ and standard deviation $\sigma/\sqrt{n}$, and is normal when the population is normally distributed

☐ know that for a large sample size the sampling distribution of the sample mean is approximately normal (the Central Limit Theorem)

☐ be able to solve problems involving the sampling distribution of the sample mean

☐ be able to solve problems involving the sampling distribution of the sample proportion

☐ know the nature of the *t*-distributions and how they relate to the standard normal distribution, $N(0,1)$

Top Tips

The field of sampling distributions forms a backbone to the whole study of statistics, and can at first seem very complicated. It is, in fact, quite easy to understand once you get clear in your mind what is really happening. So we concentrate here on helping you to get a full understanding of the ideas involved.

• *Understand the difference between population parameters and sample statistics*

Examples of population parameters are the population mean, μ, the population standard deviation, σ, and the population median (for which there is no standard notation). Examples of sample statistics are the sample mean, $\overline{x}$, the sample standard deviation, s, and the sample median. Sample statistics (sometimes called just "statistics") are used to estimate population parameters (sometimes called just "parameters"), and you should be aware that, for example, it might be suggested that you use the sample *median* to estimate the population *mean*.

Bear in mind that it is not always the population *mean* that is being estimated. For example, the sample standard deviation is designed to be an estimator for the population standard deviation.

• *Understand why the standard deviation of the sampling distribution of the sample mean is smaller than the population standard deviation*

Let's consider a very large population – all the women in a town, for example. Let the population mean height be μ.

Imagine picking a woman at random and measuring her height. Roughly how far might you expect this height to be from μ? You are estimating the population standard deviation, σ.

Now imagine picking a random sample of 20 women, and finding the sample mean height, $\overline{x}$. How far might you expect $\overline{x}$ to be from μ? The answer is a lot less than σ, since any extremely large heights in the sample are likely to be balanced out by extremely small heights in the sample.

So the standard deviation of $\overline{x}$ is less than the population standard deviation. The precise formula is that the standard deviation of $\overline{x}$ is $\sigma/\sqrt{n}$, where n is the size of the sample.

• *Understand that the Central Limit Theorem makes sense intuitively*

Imagine a very large company for which the salaries are not normally distributed but are, let's say, positively skewed. We will denote the mean salary for the company by μ.

Now imagine taking a large sample of, say, 50 salaries from this company, and finding the sample mean. We expect this sample mean to be very close to μ, since any extreme salary (in either direction) in the sample will be reduced in its impact by the majority of the other 49 salaries.

Now imagine taking many, many samples of size 50 and finding their sample means. We expect a great density of values around μ, with the density tailing off to each side of μ; looking like a normal distribution with mean μ, in fact.

Now, thinking about this carefully, you might want to argue that the distribution of the values of the sample means will be slightly positively skewed. This is in fact correct, but only very slightly, as, by the same argument as above, the effect on the sample mean of any extremely large values in the sample will be greatly reduced by the majority of other values in the sample.

You should be a little closer now to understanding why the Central Limit Theorem makes sense intuitively.

• *Understand where the t-distributions come from*

If we take a random sample of size n from a normally distributed population, then $(\bar{x} - \mu)/(\sigma/\sqrt{n})$ is normally distributed with mean 0 and standard deviation 1. If we replace the population standard deviation σ with the sample standard deviation s, we get $(\bar{x} - \mu)/(s/\sqrt{n})$, which is t-distributed with $n - 1$ degrees of freedom.

Now, the variability in $(\bar{x} - \mu)/(\sigma/\sqrt{n})$ is provided solely by $\bar{x}$, since everything else in the expression is a constant. However, when we replace the constant σ with s, we introduce more variability, since s, the sample standard deviation, has its own variability. This explains why the t-distributions have more variability than the standard normal distribution, $N(0,1)$.

Further, we can see that the larger the value of n, the less variability is attached to s, since for larger samples the sample standard deviation is a more accurate estimator of σ. So, as the number of degrees of freedom increases, the variance of the t-distribution decreases, getting closer and closer to the variance of the standard normal distribution, which is 1.

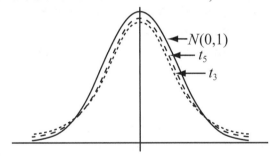

7. Confidence Intervals for Means and Proportions

You should know how to find the following intervals:

☐ z-interval for the population mean

☐ t-interval for the population mean

☐ z-interval for the population proportion

☐ z-interval for the difference between two population means

☐ two-sample t-interval for the difference between two population means

☐ paired t-interval for the difference between two population means

□ *z*-interval for the difference between two population proportions

Additionally, you should know how to:

□ interpret a confidence interval

□ interpret a confidence level

□ find the minimum sample size for a given margin of error

✎ *Top Tips*

• *When asked to construct a confidence interval, perform all three steps*

This is very important. Any time you are asked for a confidence interval, you need to do the following:

1. Name the type of interval and check the conditions

    So you will need to say, for example, "This is a *t*-interval for the population mean," and then check the conditions for that type of interval. We will look at the details of how you should check the conditions in the next tip.

2. Mechanics

    This is the numerical work needed to calculate the interval. You should provide the formula, the formula with the numbers plugged in, and the result.

3. Interpretation of the interval

    For example, if the question asks you to find a 95% confidence interval for the mean height of all the women in a town, a model answer is as follows:

     We are 95% confident that the mean height of all the women in the town is between 62.827 and 63.611 inches.

    Never use the words "probability" or "chance" when interpreting a confidence interval.

• *Do a complete check of the conditions*

You will first need to make a statement that we are told (or we have to assume) something about the randomness of the sample(s). In one-sample intervals we need one random sample. In two-sample intervals we need either two independent random samples, or random assignment of a set of objects to two groups (as in experiments). In a paired *t*-interval we need to know that the sample differences can be viewed as a random sample from a population of differences.

Then you will need to check the conditions for the type of interval you're calculating. There are three possibilities:

I. *z*- or *t*-intervals for population means where the sample size(s) is/are greater than 30

    In this case we are using the Central Limit Theorem, and you just need to state the sample size and note that it is greater than 30 (for a one-sample interval), or (for a two-sample interval) state both sample sizes and note that they are both greater than 30.

II. *z*- or *t*-intervals for population means where the sample size(s) is/are *not* greater than 30

Here, since we can't use the Central Limit Theorem, we are depending on the fact that the population(s) is/are normally distributed. Most likely, you will *not* be told that the population is normally distributed and you will be given the sample values. You have to justify the assumption that the population is normally distributed *by showing that the set of sample values roughly follows the pattern of a normal distribution*. This is done by drawing a graph (or pair of graphs for two-sample intervals) into your answer. If you draw a histogram or a boxplot you need to say that the distribution is roughly symmetrical and there are no outliers. If you draw a normal probability plot, you need to say that the pattern in the plot is roughly linear.

(Do not be overly concerned if your graph really doesn't look all that symmetrical (or linear, in the case of a normal probability plot). Remember that we're probably dealing with a small sample, and so some departure from symmetry in the sample values can be expected even if we're dealing with what is in fact a truly normally distributed population. If you're not certain, you should use a phrase such as "proceed with caution.")

III. *z*-intervals for population proportions

In this case you need to check (for a one-sample interval) that $n\hat{p} \geq 10$ and $n(1 - \hat{p}) \geq 10$, or (for a two-sample interval) that $n_1\hat{p}_1 \geq 10$, $n_1(1 - \hat{p}_1) \geq 10$, $n_2\hat{p}_2 \geq 10$, $n_2(1 - \hat{p}_2) \geq 10$. You need to write out the calculations for these checks – it's not enough just to say, for example, "$n\hat{p} \geq 10$ ✔, $n\hat{q} \geq 10$ ✔." (If your textbook gives a slightly different set of criteria, then it's fine to do whatever the book suggests. This applies to the numerical check in I. above, also.)

Failing to check the conditions completely when asked for a confidence interval is one of the most common mistakes on the exam, and will result in your getting at most half-credit for the confidence interval. So make absolutely sure that you do all that is required.

- *Know how to interpret the confidence <u>level</u>*

Not to be confused with interpretation of the confidence *interval*, which is Step 3 of the standard confidence interval answer, this is how to respond when you are asked, "What is the meaning of 95% confidence in this context?" Here's a model answer:

> ✏ In 95% of samples, the resulting confidence interval will contain the true mean height of all the women in the town.

Let's explain this in slightly greater detail. At this stage we have generally calculated the confidence interval on the basis of one sample. We are now imagining taking a very large number of samples and, for each sample, calculating the confidence interval in the same way. Each sample will be different, and therefore all the confidence intervals will be different. The statement is that 95% of the confidence intervals will contain the true mean height of the women.

Notice that the only numbers contained in the model answer are "95." If you include any other numbers, then you're getting something wrong!

8. Hypothesis Tests for Means and Proportions

You will need to know the following hypothesis tests:

☐ *z*-test for the population mean

- □ *t*-test for the population mean
- □ *z*-test for the population proportion
- □ *z*-test for the difference between two population means
- □ two-sample *t*-test for the difference between two population means
- □ paired *t*-test for the difference between two population means
- □ *z*-test for the difference between two population proportions

Additionally, you should know how to:

- □ distinguish between one- and two-tailed tests
- □ interpret the *p*-value
- □ use critical values
- □ use a confidence interval to make a conclusion to a hypothesis test

Top Tips

- *When performing a hypothesis test, complete all four steps*

  These are the four steps:

  1. State the hypotheses

     You might say, for example:

     $H_0: \mu = 63.5$

     $H_a: \mu > 63.5$

     It is good practice to define the parameter(s) you use. For the above example you might start by saying, "Let μ be the mean height of all the women in the town." However, if you use standard notation (μ for a population mean and p or π for a population proportion), you will get full credit for your hypotheses even if you don't define the parameter(s).

     In two-sample tests, use subscripts that refer specifically to the populations under consideration. For example, if a comparison is being made of a population of girls to a population of boys, use μ_G and μ_B rather than μ_1 and μ_2.

     You may, if you prefer, give the hypotheses in words rather than symbols, but be sure to make it clear that the hypotheses refer to *population* parameters.

  2. Name the test, and check the conditions

     So you need to say, for example, "This is a *t*-test for the population mean," and go on to check the conditions. We'll give details about how to check the conditions in the next tip.

  3. Mechanics

     First, evaluate the test statistic, showing the formula and how you plug in the numbers. Then evaluate the *p*-value. (Alternative methods using critical values are accepted, but be aware that an understanding of *p*-values *and* critical values is required in the exam.) Also, be sure to state the number of degrees of freedom where applicable.

4. Conclusion

    Here's a model conclusion:

     Since the *p*-value is 0.021, which is less than 0.05, we reject H_0. We have sufficient evidence to conclude that the mean height of all the women in the town is greater than 63.5 inches.

    Note that you do not *have* to use phrases such as "Reject / fail to reject H_0," in fact a phrase of this sort, without a conclusion in context such as the model answer above, would not be considered a complete conclusion. The conclusion must contain some reference to the size of the *p*-value ("less/greater than 0.05" or "which is small / not small"), and must be given in the context of the question. Be sure also to include the word "mean(s)" or "proportion(s)."

If your teacher has given you a different set of steps then that's fine, so long as you cover all of the above criteria.

• *Do a complete check of the conditions*

The conditions that need to be checked for hypothesis tests are almost identical to those for their equivalent confidence intervals (the exception is with the test/interval for a single proportion, where you use $n\hat{p} \geq 10$ and $n(1 - \hat{p}) \geq 10$ for the confidence interval and $np \geq 10$ and $n(1 - p) \geq 10$ for the hypothesis test). Nonetheless, we will look again at all the details here, since failure to correctly check the conditions for a hypothesis test is possibly the most common error in the exam.

You will first need to make a statement that we are told (or we have to assume) something about the randomness of the sample(s). In one-sample tests we need one random sample. In two-sample tests we need either two independent random samples, or random assignment of a set of objects to two groups (as in experiments). In a paired *t*-interval we need to know that the sample differences can be viewed as a random sample from a population of differences.

Then you will need to check the conditions for the type of test you're calculating. There are three possibilities:

I. *z*- or *t*-tests for population means where the sample size(s) is/are greater than 30

    In this case we are using the Central Limit Theorem, and you just need to state the sample size and note that it is greater than 30 (for a one-sample test), or (for a two-sample test) state both sample sizes and note that they are both greater than 30.

II. *z*- or *t*-tests for population means where the sample size(s) is/are *not* greater than 30

    Here, since we can't use the Central Limit Theorem, we are depending on the fact that the population(s) is/are normally distributed. Most likely, you will *not* be told that the population is normally distributed and you will be given the sample values. You have to justify the assumption that the population is normally distributed *by showing that the set of sample values roughly follows the pattern of a normal distribution*. This is done by drawing a graph (or pair of graphs for two-sample tests) into your answer. If you draw a histogram or a boxplot you need to say that the distribution is roughly symmetrical and there are no outliers. If you draw a normal probability plot, you need to say that the pattern in the plot is roughly linear.

(Do not be overly concerned if your graph really doesn't look all that symmetrical (or linear, in the case of the normal probability plot). Remember that we're probably dealing with a small sample, and so some departure from symmetry in the sample values can be expected even if we're dealing with what is in fact a truly normally distributed population. If you're not certain, you should use a phrase such as "proceed with caution.")

III. *z*-tests for population proportions

In this case you need to check (for a one-sample test) that $np \geq 10$ and $n(1-p) \geq 10$, or (for a two-sample test) that $n_1 \hat{p}_1 \geq 10$, $n_1(1-\hat{p}_1) \geq 10$, $n_2 \hat{p}_2 \geq 10$, $n_2(1-\hat{p}_2) \geq 10$. You need to write out the calculations for these checks – it's not enough just to say, for example, "$np \geq 10$ ✔, $n(1-p) \geq 10$ ✔." (If your textbook gives a slightly different set of criteria, then it's fine to do whatever the book suggests. This applies to the numerical check in I. above, also.)

- *Never "Accept* H_0*"*

To accept H_0 in the example in the first tip would be to say that the mean height of all the women in the town is exactly 63.5 inches, to an infinite number of decimal places. This is obviously a very strong statement, and one that cannot be justified. We only ever *have* convincing evidence or *do not have* convincing evidence of whatever is stated in H_a (and remember to give everything in your conclusion in *words*, as demonstrated in Part 4 of the first tip).

- *Know how to distinguish between the two-sample t-test and the paired t-test*

This applies to confidence intervals, also. Particularly when the correct test is the paired version, students over the years have been very poor at making the correct choice.

We're talking here about comparing means. If you have two samples, then it's a two-sample *t*-test. If you have one sample, with two numbers for each element of the sample, then it's a paired *t*-test. It's also a paired *t*-test if the data come from an experiment where the set of experimental units has been split into blocks of size 2 (matched pairs).

- *Know how to check the conditions for the paired t-test*

In this hypothesis test you work out the differences for the sample values, and test whether the mean difference is significantly less than, greater than, or different from zero. In order to do this, you need to justify the assumption that the population of differences is normally distributed. This is done by drawing a boxplot, histogram, or normal probability plot for the sample *differences*, and commenting in the same way as in option II in the tip above on checking the conditions. (You also, of course, have to state that we know or we assume that the set of sample differences is a random sample from the population of differences.)

- *Know how to interpret the p-value*

This is actually what hypothesis testing is all about, so we'll spend a little time on it.

We use hypothesis testing intuitively every day of our lives. Consider the following example:

Let's suppose that my wife leaves work at 4 p.m. every day. She either drives straight home (the journey takes about 20 minutes) or she runs some errands (of varying lengths).

If it gets to 4:25 p.m. and she's not yet home, I think to myself, "Given that she drove straight home, it's still quite possible that she would not be home by now." So I do not have evidence that she's running errands.

If, however, it gets to 4:40 p.m. and she's still not home, I think to myself, "Given that she drove straight home it's very unlikely that she would not be home by now." So I have evidence that she's running errands.

The *p*-value in the context of this example is the probability, given that she drove straight home, that she would not be home by now. When it gets to as late as 4:40 p.m. this *p*-value is small, so I reject the null hypothesis that she drove straight home in favor of the alternative hypothesis that she is running errands.

If you understand this example (which I hope you do!), you understand hypothesis testing.

When you are asked to interpret the *p*-value, you have to state that its value (0.021, for example) is the probability, given that H_0 is true, that the test statistic would be as large (or small – or different from zero for a two-tailed test) as the one obtained. As always, this statement must be given in the context of the question. So here's a model interpretation, when the *t*-statistic is 2.180 and the *p*-value is 0.021:

 0.021 is the probability, given that the mean height of all the women in the town is 63.5 inches, that you would get a value of *t* as large as 2.180.

Remember that the *t*-statistic measures essentially the distance of the sample mean from the supposed population mean. So a slightly less precise but acceptable interpretation would be to say, "0.021 is the probability, given that the mean height of all the women in the town is 63.5 inches, that you would get a sample mean as far above 63.5 as the one obtained in our sample."

- *Know precisely how to use a confidence interval to make a conclusion to a hypothesis test*

Let's assume that you have found, or have been given, a 95% confidence interval for the difference of two population means or proportions.

If zero is in the confidence interval, then we do not have convincing evidence of a difference in the population means (or proportions) at the 5% level.

If zero is *not* in the confidence interval, then we *do* have convincing evidence of a difference in the population means (or proportions) at the 5% level.

This is easy to understand, since, if zero is not in the confidence interval, then it is not feasible that the difference in the population parameters is zero, or, in other words, we have convincing evidence of a difference in the population parameters. Notice that the conclusion we're getting from the confidence interval is for a *two-tailed* test.

9. The Chi-Square Tests

You should know how to perform the following three chi-square tests:

- ☐ goodness of fit
- ☐ independence
- ☐ homogeneity

Top Tips

- *Know how to distinguish between the three tests*

  In the goodness of fit test there is one categorical variable, whereas in the tests for independence and homogeneity there are two. So, for example, the information given in a question on goodness of fit could be:

Color of Car	White	Black	Silver	Red	Other
Number of Cars Observed	101	62	54	50	120

  The information given in a question on independence or homogeneity could be as in the following table, where the numbers in the table are counts of people:

	Disagree	No Opinion	Agree
Male	78	33	49
Female	66	55	39

  So, in the first example there is one variable (color of car), and in the second there are two variables (gender and opinion).

  All that remains now, therefore, is to be able to tell the difference between the tests for independence and homogeneity. A question on independence is likely to say something like, "Is there any evidence of an association between gender and opinion?" A question on homogeneity is likely to say something like, "Is there any evidence that the three category proportions are different for the two populations (males and females)?" The wording can vary, but the hard and fast way to tell between the two tests is as follows: If the counts in the table resulted from *one* sample then it would be a test for independence. If the counts resulted from *two* samples – a random sample of males and a random sample of females – it would be a test for homogeneity. Tests for independence always involve a single sample; tests for homogeneity involve two or more samples.

  Once you have decided which test to perform, you will need to make sure that you use the correct wording. We'll leave you to look back in your class notes or your textbook and to learn exactly what you have to say.

  Notice that in chi-square tests the numbers given are counts. In tests for proportions you are given counts or sample proportions. If the numbers given are measurements (or scores), then the hypothesis tests available to us are the tests for means and the test for the slope of the regression line.

- *Complete all four steps of the hypothesis test*

  The four steps for hypothesis tests given in the previous section apply to chi-square tests, also.

  In Step 2, the conditions to check are that the observed counts result from one (or more than one) random sample, and that the expected counts (which you should give in your answer) are all greater than 5. (There are variations on this latter criterion – it's fine to use whatever your textbook says.)

Be careful to word your conclusion (Step 4) correctly. If you are failing to reject H_0, then a correct answer could involve a double negative – for example, "We do not have convincing evidence that the proportions of car colors are not the same as the published proportions." Whatever you do, don't "accept H_0"!

- *Know how to perform the numerical steps of the chi-square tests on your calculator*

The calculator can be a significant time-saving device in this area of the syllabus, particularly with the tests for independence and homogeneity, so it's worth making sure that you know how to use it to perform these tests.

For the goodness of fit test, be aware that different calculators deal with the test in different ways, so make sure that you are familiar with the way to do it on *your* calculator.

In the tests for independence and homogeneity, the calculator will find the expected frequencies and will calculate the test statistic and the *p*-value for you. Make sure you know to achieve this!

You should also be aware that a multiple-choice question could test your ability to perform certain steps – for example, finding expected frequencies or the *p*-value – *without* using the chi-square test function on the calculator. So be sure that you can do this, also.

10. Inference for the Slope of the Regression Line

You should know how to

- □ perform the hypothesis test and find the confidence interval for the slope of the regression line using computer output
- □ perform the hypothesis test (and possibly find the confidence interval) using raw data
- □ interpret the values of s and s_b

 Top Tips

- *Know how to use computer output*

Let's use an example for this. Suppose that a large number of students in a college take algebra. One year, at the end of the first quarter, a random sample of 20 students is taken, and the students in the sample are given a surprise exam. A list is compiled containing the quarter averages and the exam scores for those 20 students, and a linear regression is run, with the following results:

```
                Dependent variable: Exam
Predictor         Coef         SE Coef        T            P
Constant        46.063584(1)   20.19293      2.28         0.0349
Quarter         0.3063584(2)   0.236814(3)   1.29(4)      0.2121(5)

S = 4.7749(6)   R-sq = 8.51%   R-sq (adj) = 3.42%
```

There are six numbers in the table that we should be concerned with here, and we will look at their relevance now.

(1) 46.064 is the *y*-intercept for the least squares regression line; that is, the value of *a* in $\hat{y} = a + bx$.

(2) 0.306 is the slope of the least squares regression line; that is, the value of *b* in $\hat{y} = a + bx$.

(3) 0.237 is the standard error of the slope of the regression line, often denoted by s_b.

(4) 1.29 is the value of the *t*-statistic in the *t*-test for the slope of the regression line (with null hypothesis H_0: $\beta = 0$).

(5) 0.212 is the *p*-value in the *t*-test for the slope of the regression line. It is important to note that this *p*-value is for the *two-tailed* test.

(6) 4.775 is the standard error about the least squares regression line, usually denoted by *s*.

- *Understand the meanings of s and s_b*

The formula for *s*, the standard error about the regression line, is $s = \sqrt{\dfrac{\sum(y - \hat{y})^2}{n - 2}}$. This

quantity is a measure of the amount by which the points in the scatterplot vary vertically from the least squares regression line. Now, if we replace $(n - 2)$ by $(n - 1)$ in the formula for *s*, we

get $\sqrt{\dfrac{\sum(y - \hat{y})^2}{n - 1}}$, which is the standard deviation of the residuals. Therefore *s*, being very close

to this quantity, can itself be referred to as the standard deviation of the residuals. So, if you were asked to interpret the value of *s* for the example in the previous tip, you could say:

> 🖉 4.775 is the standard deviation of the residuals for the students' exam scores.

The formula for s_b, as given on the formula sheet provided in the exam, is $s_b = \dfrac{\sqrt{\dfrac{\sum(y - \hat{y})^2}{n - 2}}}{\sqrt{\sum(x - \overline{x})^2}}$,

but you are unlikely to be expected to use this formula. In order to understand what s_b represents, we need to think in the following way: In the example in the previous tip, one sample of 20 students was taken, and the regression line was found. Imagine now taking a very large number of samples, and finding the slope of the regression line for each. The statistic s_b is an estimate of the standard deviation of this set of slopes of regression lines. So here's a model interpretation of s_b:

> 🖉 0.237 is an estimate of the standard deviation of the slopes of the regression lines relating exam score and quarter score over all possible samples of 20 students.

- *Know how to perform the hypothesis test and construct the confidence interval*

The first thing to remember is that you should complete all four steps of the hypothesis test as given in Section 8 or, for the confidence interval, all three steps as given in Section 7. We will look at how to check the conditions in the next tip.

If you're given computer output, then, for the hypothesis test, you can use the *t*-value and the *p*-value given. (We saw how to locate these values in the first tip of this section.) For the confidence interval, state the formula $b \pm t * \cdot s_b$, and use the values of b and s_b given in the computer output, along with the value of $t*$ given in the table of t critical values provided with the exam. (Note that the number of degrees of freedom is $n - 2$, where n is the sample size.)

If you are *not* given computer output, then you will need to use the raw data provided. For the hypothesis test, you can calculate the relevant quantities using the calculator function designed to do this test. Do not be concerned about including the formulas – these are very unlikely to be required.

The confidence interval, when you're not given computer output, is a little tricky to find, unless you have one of the calculators that has the inbuilt function to do this. For this reason, the confidence interval using raw data is unlikely to be required in the exam.

- *Know how to check the conditions*

These are what textbooks call the "conditions (or assumptions) for the regression model." The concepts behind these conditions are sometimes considered complex, but the process of checking them is relatively straightforward.

We use the residual plot. Just as when we're checking for the appropriateness of a linear model, we are looking for a "random pattern," and here we're looking for randomness in two senses.

First, we need to check that there is no obvious curve. (Be reasonably tolerant – it's very hard to find a residual plot that doesn't show *some* evidence of a curve.)

Second, we need to check that we do <u>*not*</u> have one of the two following patterns:

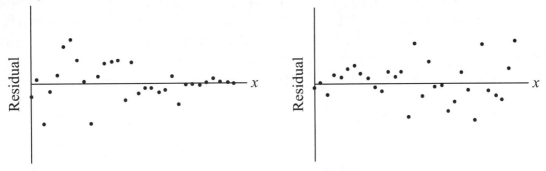

11. Errors in Hypothesis Testing

You should:

- ☐ know the meanings of Type I and Type II errors
- ☐ be able to describe Type I and Type II errors in a given context
- ☐ be able to compare the consequences of the two errors in a given context
- ☐ understand how the probabilities of Type I and Type II errors work
- ☐ know the meaning of *power*

Top Tips

- *When comparing consequences, consider both types of error*

We already looked at this in the context of free-response questions in general, when talking about how to compare two things. Suppose that you are asked, in a particular scenario, which of the errors is more serious, and you believe that it is the Type II error. Then it's important that you not only describe why a Type II error could have serious consequences, but *also* describe why the consequences of a Type I error are not so serious.

- *Understand how the probabilities of Type I and II errors work*

Here's an easy way to think about this:

1. The probability of a Type I error is always the significance level of the test.

2. Therefore, you can reduce the probability of a Type I error by reducing the significance level. However, doing this will *increase* the probability of a Type II error, since reducing the significance level increases the probability that you will fail to reject H_0. When adjusting the significance level, if you gain with Type I errors then you lose with Type II errors, and vice versa.

3. The only way to decrease the probability of a Type II error without increasing the probability of a Type I error is to increase the sample size.

And there's one more thing you should be aware of:

The probability of a Type II error is different according to the true value of the population parameter being tested. Say, for example, that you are testing H_0: $\mu = 64.5$ against H_a: $\mu > 64.5$. If μ takes a value just above 64.5, such as 64.6, then H_a is true, but it's very unlikely that you will (correctly) reject H_0; in other words, there's a *high* probability of a Type II error. If, however, the true value of μ takes a value that is much larger than 64.5, such as 66.5, then it is very likely that you will (correctly) reject H_0; in other words, there's a *low* probability of a Type II error.

Using the TI-Nspire on the AP Statistics Examination

by Heather Overstreet

This chapter will give you guidelines and tips for efficiently using the TI-Nspire calculator on the AP Statistics exam. The main focus is to provide condensed instructions for the functionality of the Nspire that you may use. First we will look at the four strands of the AP Statistics curriculum, and each of these strands has been broken into the specific topics that could arise on the exam. We will then look at the formula sheet that is provided on the AP exam, and the associated Nspire functions will be explained. Finally, we will look at the sort of multiple choice questions that might arise on the exam where the calculator is necessary or useful.

"BIG IDEAS" have also been included to provide important technology tips for the exam.

The TI-Nspire has had three different keypads: the Clickpad, the Touchpad, and the new CX. The Clickpad and Touchpad are interchangeable with the original handheld; however, the CX is the new Nspire with a slimmer design and a full color, backlit display. The instructions in this chapter use the CX keys; however, the key structure, as shown below, is exactly like the Touchpad with the exception of key shape.

 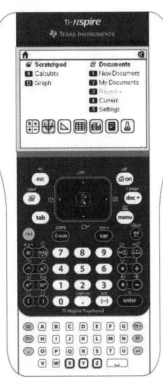 

Instructions for the Clickpad will be given in parentheses if the keystrokes vary from the Touchpad or CX.

There are three main applications on the Nspire that are used in Statistics: *Lists & Spreadsheet*, *Data & Statistics*, and *Scratchpad* (or Calculator).

- In the *Lists & Spreadsheet* application, data sets can be entered into the columns. It is very important that each column (data set) be given a name at the top of the column. The cell just below the heading is the formula cell. On the AP exam, you will probably not need this cell.

- Once a data set has been entered and named in the *Lists & Spreadsheet* page, a *Data & Statistics* page can graph it.

- The *Scratchpad* application is for quick calculations; this is the basic calculator screen. However, variables that are defined in a *Lists & Spreadsheet* page are not available in the *Scratchpad*. If the calculations require defined variables you will need to add a *Calculator* page.

Some Keystrokes that are Helpful to Remember

[ctrl] [esc] – undoes the last command. If you are computer savvy, you can also use [ctrl] [Z] which is the computer command to UNDO and [ctrl] [Y] to REDO the last command.

[ctrl] ◀ or ▶ - navigates between the pages or applications.

[▦] ((⌂) (A)) - goes directly to the calculator Scratchpad

[ctrl] [menu] – accesses the shortcut menu, which is similar to the "right-click" on the computer mouse.

THE TOPIC AREAS

I. Exploring Data: What to do with a data set

BIG IDEA 1   Just because there is a data set, you do NOT necessarily need the calculator. READ and INTERPRET the problem before you start entering data into the calculator.

Here is a data set for the average number of hours of sleep per night for 20 AP Statistics students:

8	6.5	3	7	9	6.5	6	7	7.5	7
6	8	5	7.5	7	5.5	6	7	8	6

- Open a new document.

- Insert a *Lists & Spreadsheet* page: Press ⌈ctrl⌉ ⌈I⌉ and scroll down to *Add Lists & Spreadsheet*, and press ⌈enter⌉.

- Name column A: **sleep** and enter the data above.

A. Summary Statistics

- In the *Lists & Spreadsheet* page, press ⌈menu⌉, *Statistics, Stat Calculations, One-Variable Statistics*.

- ⌈tab⌉ to ⌈OK⌉ and press ⌈enter⌉.

- Set up the next dialogue box as shown.

- Press ⌈enter⌉ and the summary statistics will be displayed.

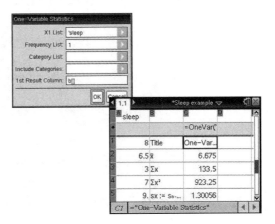

B. Graphical Displays: One data set

When graphing a data set, the Nspire does an excellent job of labeling the axes. If you are asked to display a graph on the exam, what you draw should match what you see on the screen. Always label and scale your axes!

- Insert a *Data & Statistics* page - [ctrl] [I] , arrow to *Add Data & Statistics* and press [enter] .

- Press [tab] and *Click to Add Variable* on the horizontal axis will show the variables available. Select **sleep**.

  The data points will now move into a dotplot. This is the *default* display.

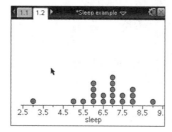

- To change the display, arrow up to an empty space in the graph. Press [ctrl] [menu] and you should see the options *Box Plot*, *Histogram*, *Normal Probability Plot*, and *Zoom*. Select each one to get the different graphical display. The Box Plot and Histograms are displayed below.

BOX PLOT

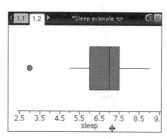

HISTOGRAM

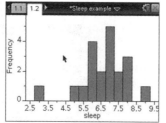

To change the width of the bars of the histogram press [ctrl] [menu] and select *Bin Settings*. You can change the Width and the Alignment to get a different display.

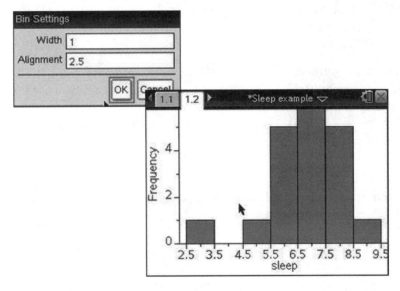

You may need to adjust the vertical axis if the bars extend beyond the top of the page. This can be done as follows.

o Using the touchpad, move the arrow to the vertical axis. You should see the arrow change to a double arrow.

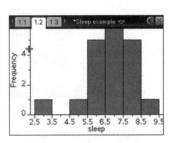

o When the double arrow appears, press and hold [✋] until a closed hand appears (✋).

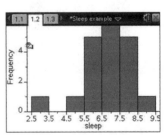

o Use the touchpad to adjust the axis. Press [✋] when the tallest bar is completely visible and the hand will become the double arrow again.

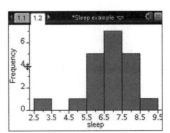

C. Graphical Displays: Comparing Data Sets

When you are asked to graph two univariate data sets, don't forget to LABEL both variables being displayed. Properly named lists in the Nspire will illustrate this idea.

Let's compare the number of hours of sleep between the AP Statistics students and a group of AP Calculus students. Below are the hours of sleep reported by 16 AP Calculus students.

9.6	5	5.5	5	7	5	6	7
6	6.5	6	6.5	6	5.5	7	6.5

- Insert another *Lists & Spreadsheet* page by pressing $\boxed{\text{ctrl}}$ $\boxed{\text{I}}$ and selecting *Add Lists & Spreadsheet*. Name column A: **aps_sleep** and press $\boxed{\text{enter}}$. In the formula cell, press $\boxed{\text{enter}}$ and select **sleep**. Name column B: **apc_sleep** and enter the 16 times.

- Insert a *Data & Statistics page*. Press $\boxed{\text{tab}}$ and *Click to Add Variable* on the horizontal axis will show the variables available. Select **aps_sleep**.

- Arrow over the **aps_sleep** and press $\boxed{\text{ctrl}}$ $\boxed{\text{menu}}$. Arrow to *Add X Variable, press* $\boxed{\text{enter}}$, and select **apc_sleep**. Both dotplots will now be displayed.

  The graphical displays can be changed using the instructions given in Section B, above.

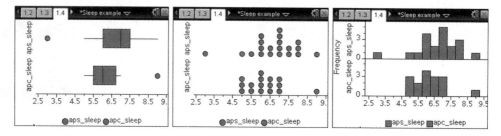

D. Bivariate Data

Students were asked how many hours per week they studied for a particular class during a grading period. The students' numerical grades are listed below along with the number of reported hours they studied each week.

Study Time	0.5	5	2	3	5	0	3	3.5	4
Grades	68	92	77	72	98	60	75	82	88

- Input the data into a new *Lists & Spreadsheet* page. Name column A: **studytime** and column B: **grades**.

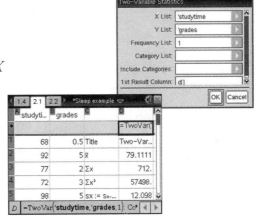

- Generate the summary statistics for variables: Press menu , *Statistics*, *Stat Calculations*, *Two-Variable Statistics*. In the dialogue box select **studytime** for the *X list* and **grades** for the *Y List*. tab to OK and press enter .

- Display the data in a scatterplot: Insert a *Data & Statistics* page. Press tab and *Click to Add Variable* on the horizontal axis will show the variables available. Select **studytime** for the horizontal axis. Press tab again and *Click to Add Variable* on the vertical axis will show the variables available. Select *grades* for the vertical axis.

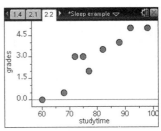

- Insert the least squares regression line: Press menu , *Analyze*, *Regression*, *Show Linear* $(a + bx)$.

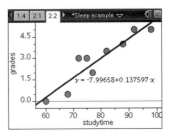

- Look at the residual plot to verify linearity of the model: Press menu, *Analyze, Residuals, Show Residual Plot*. The residual plot will appear below the scatterplot in a split window.

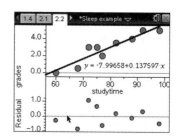

II. Sampling & Experimental Design

Selecting a Random Sample OR Random Assignment

You need to select 5 participants for a survey. There are 15 people available:

Adison	Bentley	Carter	Davids	Edwards
Francis	Granger	Hathaway	Ivers	Johnson
Keller	Lohman	Morris	Nance	Owens

- If you are given a list of individuals from which a sample is to be taken, the Nspire can randomly sample from this list, with OR without replacement.

- Insert a *Lists & Spreadsheet* page, and enter the subjects in the list.

BIG IDEA 4

On the AP Exam, it is unlikely that you would be expected to use a calculator to select a random sample. However, if you were, you could save precious time by numbering each subject and populating the list with these numbers.

1 – Adison	2 – Bentley	3 –Carter	4 – Davids	5 – Edwards
6 – Francis	7 – Granger	8 – Hathaway	9 – Ivers	10 – Johnson
11 – Keller	12 – Lohman	13 – Morris	14 – Nance	15 – Owens

- In a *Lists & Spreadsheet* page, name an empty column: **subjects**. Press enter twice, and in the formula bar type $\text{seq}(x, x, 1, 15)$. Then press enter again and the fifteen numbers should now be in the list.

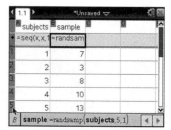

In the next column, enter the name: **sample**. Press [enter] twice and in the formula bar type *randsamp*(**subjects**, 5, 1). Then press [enter] again and five numbers are chosen without replacement from **subjects**.

According to the random sample selection in the screen shot the following subjects were chosen for the sample: Granger, Carter, Hathaway, Johnson, and Morris.

III. Probability

A. Simulation

Some problems in statistics can be analyzed using simulation of a variable. We will look here at three of the Nspire's random number generators, each based on a specific distribution.

- To access the random number generators, go to the calculator scratchpad by pressing [🖩] or insert a *Calculator* page.

- Press [menu], *Probability*, *Random*. A synopsis of the functions is listed below.

    → **RandInt** – this functions generates integers over a defined range.

    Command: randInt(lower bound, upper bound [, # of integers])

    Example: randInt(1, 28, 10) will produce 10 randomly selected integers between 1 and 28, inclusive.

    → **RandBin** – this function generates values from a binomial distribution.

    Command: randBin(n, p, [# of values])
      n = number of trials
      p = probability of success on each trial

    Example: randBin(20, 0.2, 5) will produce 5 integers from a binomial distribution with 20 trials and a probability of success on each trial of 0.2.

    → **RandNorm** – this function generates values from a normal distribution.

    Command: randNorm(mean, standard deviation, [# of values])

    Example: randNorm(5, 2.1) will produce one value from a normal distribution with a mean of 5 and a standard deviation of 2.1.

In the last example, notice there is not a third value given in the command. If no value is given, the Nspire will assign the value 1 by default.

B. Distributions

- To calculate probabilities from given distributions, go to the calculator scratchpad by pressing 〔▦〕 or insert a *Calculator* page.

- Press 〔menu〕, *Statistics*, *Distributions*. A synopsis of the functions is listed below with the dialogue box.

    → normCdf(lowBound, upBound, μ, σ) – calculates the probability of a normally distributed random variable with the mean and standard deviation specified lying between the lower and upper bounds entered.

    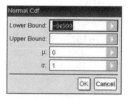

    → invNorm(Area, μ, σ) – gives the particular value of a normally distributed random variable for a given area.

    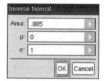

    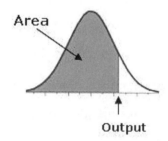

    → tCdf(lowBound,upBound,df) – calculates the probability of a *t* statistic lying in the given range for a *t* distribution with the number of degrees of freedom entered.

    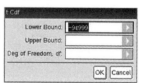

    → invt(Area, df) – gives the *t* statistic for a given probability for the number of degrees of freedom entered.

    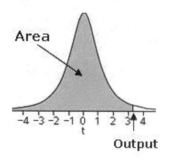

→ χ^2Cdf(lowBound,upBound,df) – calculates the probability that a χ^2 statistic lies between the bounds entered, for the number of degrees of freedom specified.

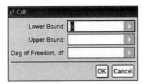

→ binomPdf(n, p, XVal) – calculates the probability that a particular number of successes, X, will occur, when there are n trials and the probability of success on each trial is p.

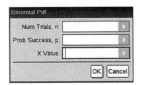

→ binomCdf(n, p, lowBound, upBound) – calculates the probability that the number of successes, X, will lie between lowbound and upbound (inclusive), when there are n trials and the probability of success on each trial is p.

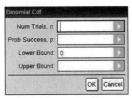

→ geomPdf(p, XVal) – calculates the probability that it takes X tries until a success for the entered probability of success, p.

→ geomCdf(p, lowBound, upBound) – calculates the probability that the number of trials to achieve a success, X, lies between lowBound and upBound (inclusive).

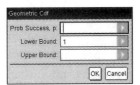

IV. Inference

A. Confidence Intervals

Press menu, *Statistics*, *Confidence Intervals*

Each type of confidence interval calculation available on the Nspire is listed in the screen shot to the right.

Notice that the *z* Interval and 2-Sample *z* Interval are crossed off. These calculations are unlikely to be necessary on the AP exam.

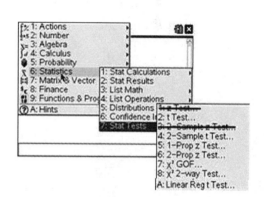

B. Hypothesis Tests

Press menu, Statistics, Stat Tests.

Each type of hypothesis test that you have learned in AP Statistics is available on the Nspire and is listed in the screen shot to the right.

Notice that the *z* Test and 2-Sample *z* Test are crossed off. These tests are unlikely to be necessary on the AP exam since knowing the population standard deviation, σ, when the population mean is unknown, is unrealistic.

All of the inference procedures shown in the screenshots above are outlined on the formula sheet that is provided with the exam. In the next section, the formula sheet has been annotated with the appropriate commands for the Nspire. Further reminders and suggestions have also been included.

THE AP STATISTICS FORMULA SHEET AND ASSOCIATED TI-NSPIRE FUNCTIONALITY

To access the Stats menu: Press $\boxed{\text{menu}}$ → Statistics

Below are the formulas that are provided with the AP exam. Additionally, descriptions are given as to how to access the associated functions on the Nspire.

I. Descriptive Statistics

One-variable

$$\bar{x} = \frac{\sum x_i}{n}$$ Mean of a data set

$$s_x = \sqrt{\frac{1}{n-1}\sum(x_i - \bar{x})^2}$$ Standard deviation of a data set

$$s_p = \sqrt{\frac{(n_1 - 1)s_1^2 + (n_2 - 1)s_2^2}{(n_1 - 1) + (n_2 - 1)}}$$ Pooled standard deviation for two samples (rarely required on the AP exam)

One-variable statistics:

Mean, standard deviation, five-number summary…

These numerical summaries are easiest to calculate in the *Lists & Spreadsheet* application.

Press $\boxed{\text{menu}}$, *Statistics, Stat Calculations, One-Variable Statistics.*

Results

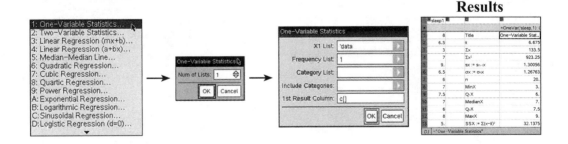

Two-variable

$$\hat{y} = b_0 + b_1 x$$ Equation of the least squares regression line

$$b_1 = \frac{\sum (x_i - \overline{x})(y_i - \overline{y})}{\sum (x_i - \overline{x})^2}$$ Slope of the LSRL

$$b_0 = \overline{y} - b_1 \overline{x}$$ y-intercept of the LSRL

$$r = \frac{1}{n-1} \sum \left(\frac{x_i - \overline{x}}{s_x} \right) \left(\frac{y_i - \overline{y}}{s_y} \right)$$ Correlation

$$b_1 = r \frac{s_y}{s_x}$$ Finding slope using correlation

$$s_{b_1} = \frac{\sqrt{\dfrac{\sum (y_i - \hat{y}_i)^2}{n-2}}}{\sqrt{\sum (x_i - \overline{x})^2}}$$ Standard error of the slope estimate

Two-Variable Statistics, Linear Regression; $\overline{x}, \overline{y}, r, \hat{y}$...

The numerical summaries and linear regression equation for bivariate data are best calculated in the *Lists & Spreadsheet* application.

Press menu, *Statistics, Stat Calculations, Two-Variable Statistics* or *Linear Regression* $(a + bx)$.

Two Variable Statistics

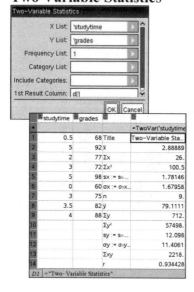

Linear Regression

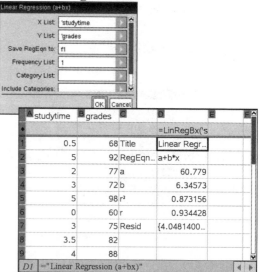

II. Probability

$$P(A \cup B) = P(A) + P(B) - P(A \cap B)$$
Probability that at least one of the events A, B occurs

$$P(A \mid B) = \frac{P(A \cap B)}{P(B)}$$
Probability that event A occurs given that B occurs

$$E(X) = \mu_x = \sum x_i p_i$$
Expected value of random variable X

$$\text{Var}(x) = \sigma_x^2 = \sum (x_i - \mu_x)^2 p_i$$
Variance of random variable X

> **REMEMBER**: *The expected value of the sum of any two random variables is the sum of the expected values of the two random variables, and the expected value of the difference of two random variables is the difference of their expected values. However, if two independent random variables are added or subtracted, their <u>variances</u> always ADD.*
> *Example:* $E(3X - 2Y) = 3E(X) - 2E(Y)$
> $\text{Var}(3X - 2Y) = 3^2\,\text{Var}(X) + 2^2\,\text{Var}(Y)$

If X has a binomial distribution with parameters n and p, then:

$$P(X = k) = \binom{n}{k} p^k (1-p)^{n-k}$$

$$\mu_x = np$$

$$\sigma_x = \sqrt{np(1-p)}$$

$$\mu_{\hat{p}} = p$$

$$\sigma_{\hat{p}} = \sqrt{\frac{p(1-p)}{n}}$$

If $\overline{x}$ is the mean of a random sample of size n from an infinite population with mean μ and standard deviation σ, then:

$$\mu_{\overline{x}} = \mu$$

$$\sigma_{\overline{x}} = \frac{\sigma}{\sqrt{n}}$$

Binomial Probabilities:

WORDING CLUES: "What is the probability/chance that exactly # out of #..." OR "What is the probability that more than/at least/at most # out of #...?"

NOTE: On a free response question about the binomial distribution, it is fine to use binompdf or binomcdf. However, you should be sure to state the distribution and the parameters, and provide a calculation. For example, you could use binompdf(10,0.7,6) and write: "The distribution of the number of baskets scored is binomial, with $n = 10$ and $p = 0.7$. So the probability that the player makes a score of 6, using a calculator, is 0.200."

PROBABILITY CALCULATIONS:

Press [menu], Probability, Distributions. The most frequently used distributions are binomial, normal, t, and χ^2.

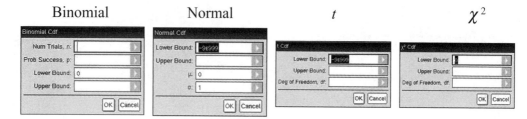

Binomial	Normal	t	χ^2

III. Inferential Statistics

Confidence interval:

Statistic $\pm$ (critical value) $\cdot$ (standard deviation of statistic)

Press menu, *Statistics*, *Confidence Intervals*

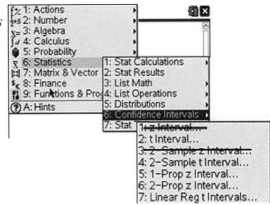

Calculator screens for confidence interval calculations

Proportions

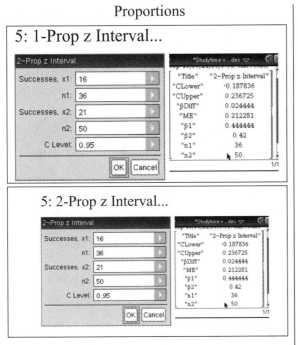

5: 1-Prop z Interval...

5: 2-Prop z Interval...

Means

2: t Interval...

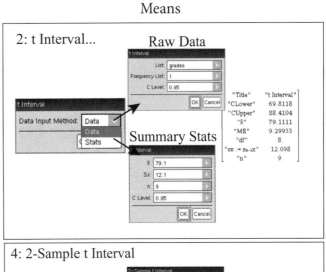

4: 2-Sample t Interval

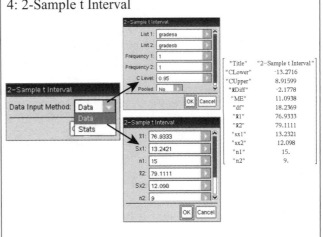

Standardized test statistic: $\dfrac{\text{statistic} - \text{parameter}}{\text{standard deviation of statistic}}$

Press menu, *Statistics*, *Stat Tests*.

THESE FORMULAS ARE NOT ON THE FORMULA SHEET:

One-proportion z-test: $z = \dfrac{\hat{p} - p}{\sqrt{\dfrac{p(1-p)}{n}}}$

One-sample t-test: $t = \dfrac{\bar{x} - \mu}{\dfrac{s}{\sqrt{n}}}$

Single-Sample

Statistic	Standard Deviation of Statistic
Sample Mean	$\dfrac{\sigma}{\sqrt{n}}$

One-sample *t*-test OR Paired *t*-test

→ In the dialogue box, you will choose either **Data** or **Stats**

→ **Data**: Select the list where your *raw data* are stored. Then tab to *Alternate Hypothesis* and select the appropriate option.

→ Stats: You will need to enter $\bar{x}$, S_x, n, and the appropriate alternative hypothesis.

Sample Proportion	$\sqrt{\dfrac{p(1-p)}{n}}$

One-proportion z-test

→ In the dialogue box, enter *Successes*, n, and appropriate alternative hypothesis.

Two-Sample

Statistic	Standard Deviation of Statistic
Difference of Sample Means	$$\sqrt{\dfrac{\sigma_1^2}{n_1} + \dfrac{\sigma_2^2}{n_2}}$$ special case when $\sigma_1 = \sigma_2$ $$\sigma\sqrt{\dfrac{1}{n_1} + \dfrac{1}{n_2}}$$
Difference of Sample Proportions	$$\sqrt{\dfrac{p_1\left(1 - p_1\right)}{n_1} + \dfrac{p_2\left(1 - p_2\right)}{n_2}}$$ special case when $p_1 = p_2$ $$\sqrt{p(1 - p)}\sqrt{\dfrac{1}{n_1} + \dfrac{1}{n_2}}$$

Two-sample *t*-test

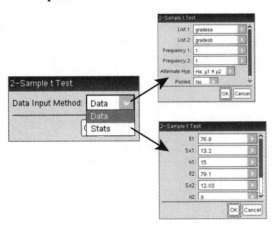

Two-proportion *z*-test

→ In the dialogue box, enter *Successes* and *n* for each proportion.

→ Select the appropriate alternative hypothesis.

χ^2-tests

Goodness of Fit:

- Enter your OBSERVED data into a column on a *Lists & Spreadsheet* page. (Be sure to name it.)

- Calculate the EXPECTED values and enter these into the next column. (Also name this one.)

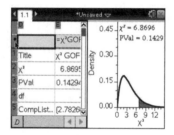

- Press menu, *Statistics*, *Stat Tests*, χ^2 *GOF*.

- Select your observed list by pressing var and arrowing up or down to the list name.

- Repeat the above step for the expected list.

- tab to OK and press enter.

Two-Way Tables:

- On a *Calculator* page, define the OBSERVED matrix:

  o Enter a name, such as: **obs** := (this symbol is obtained by pressing ctrl [◻|{◻]).

  o To enter the data into a matrix, press [◻|{◻]. In the dialogue box that appears, enter the number of rows and columns. tab to OK and press enter. A blank matrix should appear on the calculator page.

o   Enter the data corresponding the rows and columns in the data table. When you are done, press ⌊enter⌋.

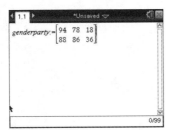

- Press ⌊menu⌋, *Statistics*, *Stat Tests*, χ^2 *2-way Test*. A dialogue box will appear asking for the *Observed Matrix*. Press ⌊var⌋ and select your observed matrix. ⌊tab⌋ to OK and press ⌊enter⌋.

The results of your inference procedure will now be displayed. To view the *Expected Matrix*, press ⌊var⌋ and select **stat.expmatrix**.

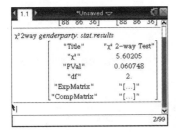

Confidence Interval for the Slope of the Population Regression Line

- Enter the data into two lists on a *Lists & Spreadsheet* page.

- Insert a *Calculator* page.

- Press ⌊menu⌋, *Statistics*, *Confidence Intervals*, *LinReg t Interval*.

  o   In the first dialogue box, select *slope*. ⌊tab⌋ to ⌊OK⌋ and press ⌊enter⌋.

o In the second dialogue box, select your *X List* and *Y List*. [tab] to [OK] and press [enter].

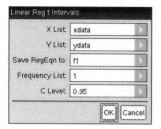

o The results should now be displayed on the *Calculator page*.

Hypothesis Test for the Slope of the Population Regression Line

- Insert a *Calculator* page.

- Press [menu], *Statistics*, *Stat Tests*, *LinReg t Test*.

  o As with the confidence interval, select your *X List* variable, and your *Y List* variable in the dialogue box.

  o Select your alternative hypothesis, [tab] to [OK], and press [enter]. The results of the test will be displayed.

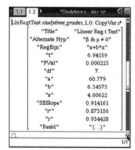

CALCULATOR-BASED SAMPLE QUESTIONS AND THEIR SOLUTIONS

The following questions are examples of multiple choice problems such as those you might see on the AP exam that either require the use of a calculator or where the calculator helps you to answer the question quickly.

1. A certain company that sells high definition TVs is considering offering a 5-year guarantee for their current model. The probability distribution for the number of complete years a TV of this type will last is shown below.

Number of Complete Years	0	1	2	3	4	5	6	7	8	9
Probability	0.10	0.12	0.03	0.14	0.32	0.12	0.08	0.05	0.03	0.01

What is the expected number of complete years that a TV of this type will last?

(A) 0.60
(B) 1.10
(C) 2.5
(D) 3.64
(E) 4

2. In a random sample of 400 adults, each person stated his or her political preference. The gender (male/female) of each respondent was also noted. The results are shown in the table below:

	Democrat	Republican	Others
Male	94	78	18
Female	88	86	36

If a chi-square test for independence is performed, what would be the contribution to the statistic from the Female Democrats?

(A) 0.0001
(B) 0.5966
(C) 0.6594
(D) 2.0643
(E) 2.2816

3. A popular brand of cereal is including 3 different types of prizes. Each box contains one prize and the manufacturer has stated that, in any given box, the three prizes are equally likely. Claire wants one of the prizes and is surprised when she has to buy 5 boxes of cereal to get it. Assuming that the boxes are independent of each other in terms of the prizes they contain, what is the probability, when a person is waiting for a particular prize, that it takes at least 5 boxes for the prize to appear?

(A) 0.1975
(B) 0.3008
(C) 0.4489
(D) 0.6992
(E) 0.7985

4. The heights of the women in a particular community are normally distributed with a mean of 64.5 inches and a standard deviation of 2.5 inches. Thirty percent of women are taller than what height?

(A) 63.2 inches
(B) 65.0 inches
(C) 65.8 inches
(D) 67.0 inches
(E) 68.0 inches

5. A local appliance rental store offers only short-term rentals and "rent-to-own" rentals. For a number of years, roughly one half of the rentals have been short-term rentals. After a change in marketing strategy, the manager of the store examines the first 50 rentals and finds that 32 of them are short-term rentals. Treating these 50 rentals as a random sample of all rentals after the change in marketing strategy, the manager performs a hypothesis test to determine whether this result provides sufficient evidence that the proportion of all rentals that are short-term is now different from a half. Which of the following is closest to the p-value for this test?

(A) 0.005
(B) 0.048
(C) 0.096
(D) 0.230
(E) 0.396

Solutions

1. **(D) 3.64**

   This question requires you to calculate the mean of a random variable. This can be done using the *Lists & Spreadsheet* application of the TI-Nspire.

   - In a *Lists & Spreadsheet*, name column A: **year** and column B: **prob**.

   - Enter the data from the table in the appropriate columns.

   - Press menu, *Statistics, Stat Calculations, One-Variable Statistics*.

   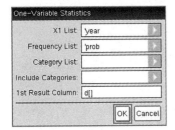

   - Select **year** for the *X List* and **prob** for the *Frequency List*. Put the results in column d.

   - tab to OK and press enter. In the resulting display, your answer will be what is listed for $\overline{x}$.

   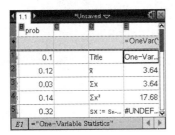

2. **(B) 0.5966**

   The Nspire will calculate a matrix with the contributions to the chi-square statistic.

   - On a *Calculator* page, define a matrix:

     - Type **genderparty**, and press ctrl := and then press .

- Select 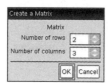 and enter 2 rows and 3 columns.

- Enter the data from the table in the matrix and press [enter].

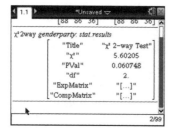

• Press [menu], *Statistics*, *Stat Tests*, χ^2 *2-way Test*.

- In the dialogue box, select **genderparty** for the *Observed Matrix*.

- [tab] to OK and press [enter].

- The results of the test will be displayed.

- To view the contributions (or component) matrix, press [var] and select **stat.compmatrix**.

The contribution for female democrats ⟶

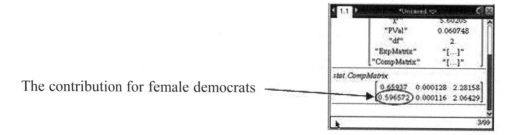

Note: If you have already performed stat functions, select the most recent **stat** variables.

3. **(A) 0.1975**

This question uses the geometric distribution, with $P(X \ge 5)$.

- On a calculator page, press [menu], *Probability, Distributions, Geometric Cdf.*

- In the dialogue window that appears, type in the *Prob success p*: 1/3, *Lower Bound* 5, *Upper Bound* 10000 (a very large number).

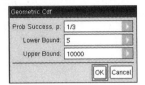

- [tab] to OK and press [enter]. The answer will be displayed.

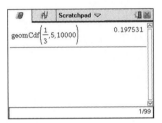

4. **(C) 65.8 inches**

Use of the Inverse Normal command will quickly determine the answer to this question. Note that the proportion of heights that are *less* than the required height is $1 - 0.30 = 0.70$.

- On a *Calculator* page, press [menu], *Statistics, Distributions, Inverse Normal.*

- In the dialogue box, enter 0.7 for *Area*, 64.5 for μ, and 2.5 for σ. [tab] to OK and press [enter].

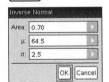

- The answer will be displayed.

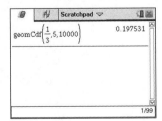

5. **(B) 0.048**

This question requires use of a 1-*proportion z-test*, with null hypothesis that the proportion of rentals that are short-term, p, is 0.5, and the alternative hypothesis that $p \neq 0.5$.

- On a *Calculator* page, press menu, *Statistics, Stat Tests, 1 Prop Z Test*.

- In the dialogue box, type 0.5 for p_0, 32 for successes, x, 50 for n, and *prop* $\neq p_0$ for the alternate hypothesis.

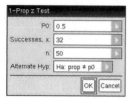

- tab to OK and press enter. The results of the test will be displayed. The p-value is displayed beside "*PVal*".

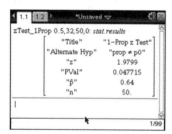

Summary Exercises

The exercises that follow cover five of the major topic areas in AP Statistics, and the questions include, in the topic areas covered, the great majority of the facts, knowledge, and skills that are required on the exam. You are encouraged to use your class notes and your textbook when completing these exercises. Be sure, also, to refer to the Top Tips for the topic area you're working on. (The Top Tips start on page 1.)

Solutions to these summary exercises are provided in the Student's Solutions Manual.

By working through these exercises, and by checking your answers in the Student's Solutions Manual, you can greatly enhance your knowledge and ability, and significantly improve your performance on the AP Statistics exam.

CORRELATION AND LINEAR REGRESSION

1. A student at a large high school conducts a study using a random sample of 20 male seniors. The student records the height (in inches) and the length of the right foot (in millimeters) of each student selected, and uses a computer to fit a least squares regression line to the data. Part of the computer output is shown below.

```
Dependent variable: Foot Length

Predictor    Coef      SE Coef      T        P
Constant     148.17    42.88        3.46     0.003
Height       1.8849    0.5964       3.16     0.005

S = 6.85709     R-sq = 35.7%     R-sq (adj) = 32.1%
```

(a) What is the value of the correlation coefficient for foot length and height?

(b) Interpret the value of the correlation coefficient that you calculated in part (a).

(c) What is the equation of the least squares regression line for predicting foot length from height?

(d) A scatterplot of the results is shown below. Draw the least squares regression line on the scatterplot.

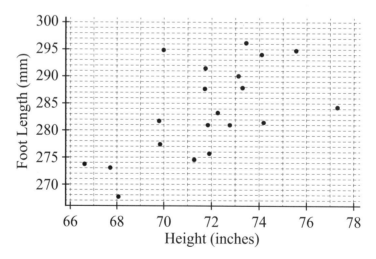

(e) Interpret the value of the slope of the least squares regression line in this context.

(f) Does the intercept of the least squares regression line have a meaningful interpretation in this context? If so, provide this interpretation. If not, explain why not.

(g) What does the least squares regression line predict for the foot length of a student whose height is 73 inches?

(h) Would it be appropriate to use the fitted regression equation to predict the foot length for a student whose height is 62 inches? Explain your answer.

(i) One of the students in the study had a height of 71.8 inches and a foot length of 291.5 millimeters. Calculate the residual for that student.

(j) Interpret the value of the residual you calculated in part (i).

(k) A residual plot for this data set is shown below.

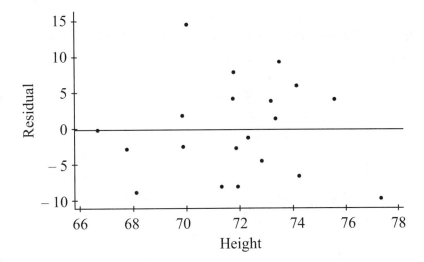

Is a line an appropriate model for the heights and foot lengths of these students? Explain how you reach your conclusion.

(l) State the value of r^2, and interpret this value in the context of this study.

(m) Note that $s = 6.85709$ in the computer output. Interpret this value in the context of this study.

(n) Identify and interpret the standard error of the slope.

(o) Suppose that a system of shoe sizes is formulated, where

$$\text{shoe size} = \frac{(\text{foot length}) - 285}{5}.$$

If, using this formula, the foot length is replaced by the shoe size for each student (with no rounding), what would be the resulting value of the correlation coefficient for shoe size and height?

2. Suppose that the heights and foot lengths of 15 high school senior girls are measured. The heights are found to have mean 63.8 inches and standard deviation 4.2 inches and the foot lengths are found to have mean 223.3 millimeters and standard deviation 12.7 millimeters. Additionally, the correlation between height and foot length for these girls is found to be 0.548. Let x = height in inches and y = foot length in millimeters.

   (a) Calculate the slope of the least squares regression line of y on x.

   (b) Calculate the y-intercept of the least squares regression line of y on x.

3. (a) Consider the data set represented by the scatterplot shown below.

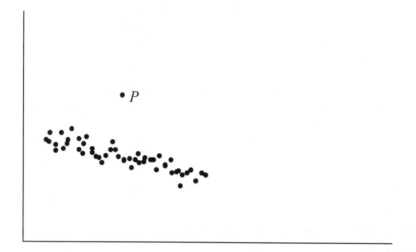

   Would removal of the point P result in a large change in the least squares regression line? Explain your answer.

   (b) Consider the data set represented by the scatterplot shown below.

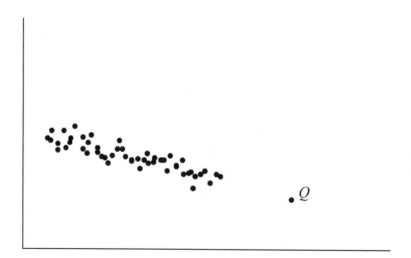

Would removal of the point Q result in a large change in the least squares regression line? Explain your answer.

(c) Consider the data set represented by the scatterplot shown below.

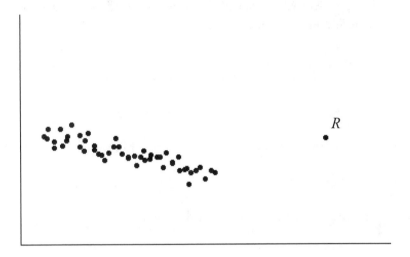

Would removal of the point R result in a large change in the least squares regression line? Explain your answer.

EXPERIMENTAL DESIGN

1. Random Assignment

An experiment is to be designed to compare two drugs, Drug A and Drug B, both designed to reduce blood pressure. (Drug A is a new formulation. Drug B is a formulation that has been used for some years.) You have been provided with 40 volunteers, all of whom suffer from high blood pressure. Twenty of the volunteers will receive Drug A, and the other 20 will receive Drug B. The reduction in blood pressure will be measured for each participant.

(a) Explain how the 40 volunteers might be randomly assigned to the two groups.

(b) Why would the volunteers be assigned *randomly* to the two groups, rather than, for example, allowing each volunteer (independently of the other volunteers) to choose which group he/she would be in?

(c) Suppose the blood pressures of the volunteers who are given Drug A are reduced significantly more, on average, than the blood pressures of the volunteers who are given Drug B. Explain why we have evidence that Drug A *causes* a greater reduction in blood pressure than Drug B.

2. Explanatory and Response Variables; Levels, Treatments

Suppose, now, that an experiment is designed to determine the effects of a particular drug <u>and</u> of exercising on people's blood pressures. Each participant will be given no drug at all, or 2mg per day of the drug, or 10 mg per day of the drug. Also, each participant will either exercise or not exercise. The reduction in blood pressure will be measured for each person who takes part in the experiment.

(a) What is/are the explanatory variable(s) in this experiment?

(b) What is/are the response variable(s) in this experiment?

(c) For each explanatory variable, how many levels are there?

(d) How many treatments are there?

(e) What/who are the experimental units in this context?

3. Control Group

Consider an experiment to determine whether regular exercise, over an extended period, reduces blood pressure. A substantial number of volunteers who suffer from high blood pressure and who do not, as yet, exercise regularly will be used in the experiment.

(a) Suppose that all the participants in the experiment are given daily sessions of supervised exercise over a period of four months, and that their blood pressures are, on average, significantly reduced. Explain why this result does <u>not</u> give us evidence that regular exercise reduces blood pressure.

(b) Suppose now that the experiment is adapted so that the participants are randomly assigned to two groups. The participants in one of the groups are given the supervised daily exercise, while those in the other group (the control group) do not exercise. How does the inclusion of the control group solve the problem described in part (a)?

4. Placebo Effect, Placebo

Consider an experiment in which a single drug, designed to reduce blood pressure, is being tested. The participants (all of whom suffer from high blood pressure) are randomly assigned to two groups: Group A and Group B. The participants in Group A will receive the drug.

(a) Suppose that the participants assigned to Group B are given no treatment at all, and that the participants in Group A undergo a significantly greater reduction in blood pressure than the participants in Group B. Explain why this does not give us evidence that the drug is effective.

(b) What, in the context of this experiment, is a placebo? Explain how use of a placebo for Group B overcomes the problem described in part (a) of this question.

5. **Lurking (Extraneous) Variables, Confounding Variables**

An experiment is designed to compare three different fertilizers, Fertilizer A, Fertilizer B, and Fertilizer C, for the growth of potted plants of a particular species. A number of very similar young plants of this species are planted in soil in identical pots. Some of the pots are treated using Fertilizer A, some using Fertilizer B, and some using Fertilizer C. At the end of the experiment the grown plants are compared using a measure of quality that includes considerations such as the number of flowers, the number of leaves, and other aspects of the health of the plant.

(a) What is the explanatory variable in this experiment?

(b) What is the response variable?

(c) A lurking (extraneous) variable is a variable that is not the explanatory variable (or the response variable), but that nonetheless might have an effect on the response variable. List three possible lurking variables in the context of this experiment.

(d) Choose one of the lurking variables you provided in part (c), and explain what would need to be the case for this variable to be described as a *confounding* variable.

6. **Generalization**

Return to the experiment described in Question 1, and assume that the 40 volunteers (who all suffered from high blood pressure) were randomly assigned to receive either Drug A or Drug B. Suppose that the blood pressures of the volunteers who were given Drug A were reduced significantly more, on average, than the blood pressures of those who were given Drug B. Can we conclude that Drug A would be more effective than Drug B for *all* patients who suffer from high blood pressure? Explain your answer.

7. **Describing an Experiment, Matched Pairs**

(a) It has been suggested that the application of lemon juice or vinegar to a sliced avocado can prevent discoloration. Suppose that you have been provided with 30 half avocadoes, recently cut. Describe a completely randomized experiment to determine which, of lemon juice or vinegar, is more effective for reducing discoloration. (Do not include a control group.)

(b) How might the experiment described in part (a) be adapted in order to make use of a matched pairs design? (Be sure to explain how the treatments would be assigned.)

(c) Why is a matched pairs design preferable to the design in part (a)?

8. **Blinding**

   (a) Return, again, to the experiment described in Question 1 where a new drug (Drug A) is compared to a current drug (Drug B), and where both drugs are designed to reduce blood pressure. A number of volunteers who suffer from high blood pressure will be randomly assigned to receive either Drug A or Drug B.

      (i) What two criteria are required for the experiment to be described as "double blind"?

      (ii) Explain why the two criteria you provided in part (a) are important in this experiment.

      (iii) What would need to be the case for the experiment to be described as "single blind"?

   (b) Suppose an experiment were to be designed to determine the effect of regular exercise on people's blood pressure. Explain why a double blind design is not possible for this experiment.

9. **Replication**

   A statistics teacher wants to compare three different teaching methods: Method A, Method B, and Method C. She decides to use her class of 18 students. Completely randomly, she will assign 6 students to Method A, 6 to Method B, and 6 to Method C. The students will be taught the same topic using these methods, and they will then all be given the same test. The three methods will be compared by comparing the average test results for the three groups.

   What problem might arise as a result of using as few as 6 students in each treatment group? Explain why using a larger class of 42 students, for example (and therefore having 14 students in each treatment group), would be preferable.

10. **Blocking**

   Return to the scenario described in the previous question, where the teacher wishes to compare the three teaching methods using her class of 18 students.

   (a) The teacher has a list of all the students' average scores in her course up to the time when she is going to start the experiment. Explain how she would conduct this experiment using blocking by average grade in the course. Use blocks of size three, and be sure to include a detailed explanation as to how the treatments would be assigned.

   (b) Explain why the block design is preferable to the completely randomized design described in the previous question.

PROBABILITY

1. A music enthusiast has a collection of recorded music consisting of 3390 albums. Each album has been classified as one of classical, jazz, or popular, and is on either CD, vinyl, or cassette. (There is only one recording of each album in the collection.) The numbers of albums falling into these categories are given in the table below.

	CD	Vinyl	Cassette	Total
Classical	846	690	81	1617
Jazz	693	562	116	1371
Popular	158	95	149	402
Total	1697	1347	346	3390

(a) An album is chosen at random from this collection. Find the probability that it is

 (i) jazz

 (ii) jazz and on vinyl

 (iii) jazz or on vinyl

 (iv) jazz, given that it is on vinyl

When an album is chosen at random from the collection, let J be the event that it is jazz and let V be the event that it is on vinyl.

(b) Are J and V mutually exclusive events?

(c) Are J and V independent events?

2. In a particular community, 80% of the people wear deodorant, 40% exercise regularly, and 84% do at least one of these two things.

(a) If a person is chosen at random from this community, what is the probability that the person wears deodorant and exercises regularly?

(b) If a person is chosen at random from this community, what is the probability that the person neither wears deodorant nor exercises regularly?

(c) What is the probability that a person in this community wears deodorant given that he/she exercises regularly?

(d) If a person is known not to wear deodorant, what is the probability that the person exercises regularly?

(e) In this community, are the events "wears deodorant" and "exercises regularly" mutually exclusive? Explain.

(f) In this community, are the events "wears deodorant" and "exercises regularly" independent? Explain.

(g) In a random sample of 1000 people from this community, how many would you expect to wear deodorant? Would <u>exactly</u> this number of people in the sample wear deodorant?

3. A student is about to take APs in US History, English Language, and Statistics. She estimates that her probabilities of getting 5's in these subjects are 0.6, 0.7, and 0.8, respectively. She is also willing to assume that her results in the three subjects are independent. Assuming that the student's estimates are correct, find the probability that she gets

(a) 5's in all three subjects

(b) no 5's

(c) exactly one 5

(d) at least one 5

4. A student named Lenny rides a bicycle to school on 3/5 of days, and on the other days is driven to school by car. When he uses the bicycle he is able to avoid traffic, and is on time to school with probability 0.95. When he is driven to school he is on time with probability 0.75.

(a) Complete the tree diagram below by writing the specified probabilities in the boxes.

(i) The probability that, on a randomly chosen day, Lenny rides his bicycle to school

(ii) The probability that, on a randomly chosen day, Lenny is driven to school

(iii) The probability that Lenny is on time, given that he rides his bicycle to school

(iv) The probability that Lenny is late, given that he rides his bicycle to school

(v) The probability that Lenny is on time, given that he is driven to school

(vi) The probability that Lenny is late, given that he is driven to school

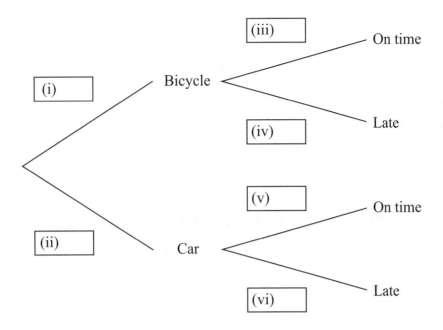

(b) If a day is chosen at random, what is the probability that, on that day, Lenny rides his bicycle to school and is on time?

(c) On what proportion of days is Lenny on time?

(d) If, on a particular day, Lenny is observed to be on time, what is the probability that Lenny rode his bicycle to school on that day?

5. A statistics teacher has 7 girls and 5 boys in her class. If the teacher chooses three students at random to record the results of a study, what is the probability that all three students are girls?

RANDOM VARIABLES

1. As part of its census, a country keeps record of the number of vehicles available to each household. Using this information, it is calculated that, when a household is chosen at random from the country, the probability distribution of the number of vehicles available is as shown below.

Number of Vehicles	0	1	2	3
Probability	0.32	0.42	0.17	0.09

(a) Calculate the mean number of vehicles per household in this country.

(b) Calculate the standard deviation of the number of vehicles available to households.

(c) The unit of currency for the country is the guilder. The government imposes a monthly tax of 320 guilders per household, plus 180 guilders for each vehicle available to the household. Using your answers to parts (a) and (b), calculate the mean and the standard deviation of the monthly tax amount (in guilders) for a randomly chosen household.

2. Jenna has started a business selling half-liter bottles of spring water. She sells the water using two methods. The first is through a small stall set up at a popular tourist location, where she sells individual bottles for cash. The second is through a web site, where customers can order cases of the bottles for local delivery. The number of bottles that she sells from the stall on a randomly selected day has mean 128 and standard deviation 16. The number of bottles she sells via the web site on a randomly selected day has mean 223 and standard deviation 35.

   (a) Calculate the expected value of the total number of bottles sold on a randomly selected day.

   (b) What assumption do you need to make in order to use the information given above to calculate the standard deviation of the total number of bottles sold on a randomly selected day? Do you consider this assumption to be reasonable? Explain.

   In the questions that follow, assume that the assumption in part (b) holds.

   (c) Calculate the standard deviation of the total number of bottles sold on a randomly selected day.

   (d) Calculate the mean and the standard deviation of the amount by which, on a randomly selected day, the number of bottles sold through the web site exceeds the number of bottles sold from the stall.

   (e) Jenna charges $1.25 per bottle at the stall and $0.57 per bottle on the web site. Calculate the mean and the standard deviation of the total amount of money she takes on a randomly selected day.

3. Nick plays basketball. When Nick takes a free throw, the probability that he is successful is 0.7. Today, Nick will take six free throws. Assuming that the outcomes of the throws are independent of each other, find the probability that he has

   (a) exactly four successes

   (b) at least four successes

4. Nick's younger brother, James, also plays basketball. For James, the probability of being successful on a free throw is 0.35. Suppose that James will take 10 free throws and that the outcomes of the throws are independent of each other.

   (a) Find the probability that James has

      (i)   no successes

      (ii) at least one success

      (iii) at least three successes

   (b) What are the mean and the standard deviation of the number of successes for James?

5. The basketball player in the previous question, James, decides to start taking free throws, and to continue until he gets his first success. Find the probability that the number of throws he takes up to and including his first success is

   (a) three

   (b) less than three

   (c) more than three

6. In a particular population of polar bears, the adult males have masses that are normally distributed with mean 515 kilograms and standard deviation 88 kilograms.

   (a) An adult male is chosen at random from this population. Calculate the probability that his mass is

      (i)   between 480 and 580 kilograms

      (ii) less than 600 kilograms

      (iii) more than 450 kilograms

   (b) What is the minimum mass required for a bear to be amongst the heaviest 20% of adult males in this population?

7. For a population of polar bears, 22% of the adult females have masses less than 240 kilograms. If the masses of adult females are known to be normally distributed with standard deviation 51 kilograms, what is the mean mass of adult females in this population?

8. For each of the following say whether the distribution of the random variable X is most likely to be binomial, geometric, normal, or none of these. ("None of these" is allowed in only one answer.)

   (a) You stand on a street in New York City and watch people using their cell phones. X is the number of phones out of the next ten that are smart phones.

   (b) X is the number of flips of a coin until you get a head.

   (c) X is the length of the next French fry that you eat.

   (d) X is the number of journeys that you make to school up to the first viewing of a car with its trunk not fully closed.

   (e) X is the score when a cube with faces numbered 1 through 6 is rolled.

   (f) You know how many coins there are in your pocket. X is the number of heads that show when you drop all the coins on the floor.

MISCELLANEOUS HYPOTHESIS TESTING

As a <u>first exercise</u>, for each of the questions below, simply state the type of hypothesis test that is required.

As a <u>second exercise</u>, perform all the tests.

1. A large pine forest is populated by three different types of pine tree: Sand Pine, Shortleaf Pine, and Loblolly Pine. It is known that 58% of the trees in the forest are Sand Pines, 22% are Shortleaf Pines, and 20% are Loblolly Pines. A random sample of 100 trees is selected from one region of the forest, and these 100 trees are categorized according to type, with the results as shown below.

Type of Pine	Sand	Shortleaf	Loblolly
Number of Trees	55	14	11

   Does this sample provide convincing evidence that the proportions of the three types of pine are different in this region of the forest from the proportions in the forest as a whole?

2. The owners of a supermarket chain are interested in promoting fruit for its health-giving properties. As a pilot study, a random sample of 200 customers is selected, and each customer in the sample is asked whether he/she believes that eating oranges is good for your health. Of these 200 customers, 186 reply "Yes," with the remainder replying "No." Does this result provide convincing evidence that more than 90% of all customers would answer "Yes" to the question?

3. Ten years ago, a survey was conducted at a large college using a random sample of 140 students. Each student was asked "If you get a poor grade and have to tell a parent, do you tell him/her by email, by phone, or do you leave it until you next see him/her in person?" A similar survey was conducted at the same college five years ago using a random sample of 119 students, and again, this year, using a random sample of 132 students. The responses to the three surveys are summarized in the table below.

	10 Years Ago	5 Years Ago	This Year
Email	13	44	64
Phone	90	45	43
In Person	37	30	25

Do these results provide convincing evidence of any difference between the populations for the three different years in terms of the distribution of preferred mode of communication?

4. At a large high school for academically talented students, a random sample of 15 students was selected to take a mathematical problem solving contest in two consecutive years. The scores for the 15 students are given below.

Student	1	2	3	4	5	6	7	8	9	10	11	12	13	14	15
Last Year	84	80	95	83	77	84	55	86	95	102	72	96	80	87	64
This Year	91	89	79	81	91	81	74	101	107	90	60	98	85	65	99

Do these results provide convincing evidence that, if all the students at the school had taken the contest on both occasions, this year's mean score would have been greater than last year's?

5. Do the results in the previous question provide convincing evidence of a useful linear relationship between last year's scores and this year's scores?

6. At a different school from the one described in question 4, a random sample of 10 students was selected to take the math contest last year, and a different random sample of 10 students was selected to take the contest this year. The results are shown below.

Last Year	74	60	82	82	104	93	73	94	82	94
This Year	94	93	111	88	99	97	96	101	73	84

Do these results provide convincing evidence that, if all the students at the school had taken the contest on both occasions, this year's mean score would have been greater than last year's?

7. Refer to the results given in the previous question. Do last year's results provide convincing evidence that, if all the students at this school had taken the contest last year, the mean score would have been less than 90?

8. In a random sample of 165 men in long-term relationships, 32 said that they had bought valentines cards for their partners. In a random sample of 178 women in long-term relationships, 52 said that they had bought valentines cards for their partners. Do these results provide sufficient evidence to conclude that men and women in long-term relationships are different in terms of the proportions who would say that they bought valentines cards for their partners?

9. A large school district offers two buses on all its routes: an early bus and a late bus. On any given morning the students are free to decide which bus to take. Some take the early bus, as it covers the route more quickly and enables the student to take part in morning activities; others take the late bus as it gives them a small amount of extra sleep. On a particular day, a random sample of 350 high school students was selected. Each student was asked which bus he/she took, and the student's grade level was noted. The numbers of students falling into the various categories were as shown below.

	9	10	11	12
Early	56	48	38	83
Late	39	52	46	64

Do these results provide convincing evidence of an association between grade level and choice of bus for high school students in the district?

Sample Examination One

SECTION I
Time—1 hour and 30 minutes
Number of questions—40
Percent of total grade—50

Directions: Solve each of the following problems, using the available space for scratch work. Decide which is the best of the choices given and fill in the corresponding oval on the answer sheet. No credit will be given for anything written in the test book. Do not spend too much time on any one problem.

1. A used car salesman deals in sedans and SUVs, and keeps note of the horsepower of each vehicle. The values for his current inventory are represented by the boxplots below.

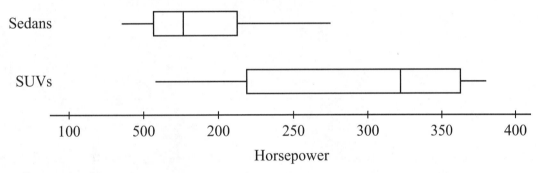

Which of the following is true?

(A) The distribution for the sedans is positively skewed and the distribution for the SUVs is negatively skewed. The range is greater for the sedans than for the SUVs.

(B) The distribution for the sedans is negatively skewed and the distribution for the SUVs is positively skewed. The range is greater for the sedans than for the SUVs.

(C) The distribution for the sedans is positively skewed and the distribution for the SUVs is negatively skewed. The range is less for the sedans than for the SUVs.

(D) The distribution for the sedans is negatively skewed and the distribution for the SUVs is positively skewed. The range is less for the sedans than for the SUVs.

(E) Both distributions are roughly symmetrical. The range is greater for the sedans than for the SUVs.

Answer

2. In order to study the effects of organic feed on the health of animals, some cows from a herd are randomly selected to be given organic feed, while the remaining cows are given a non-organic equivalent. At the end of the study the health levels of all the cows are measured. Which of the following is true?

    (A) This is an observational study in which the level of health is the explanatory variable and the type of feed is the response variable.

    (B) This is an observational study in which the type of feed is the explanatory variable and the level of health is the response variable.

    (C) This is an observational study that could establish whether organic feed causes good health.

    (D) This is an experiment in which the level of health is the explanatory variable and the type of feed is the response variable.

    (E) This is an experiment in which the type of feed is the explanatory variable and the level of health is the response variable.

Answer

3. Of the male students at a high school, 35% play football, 44% play basketball, and 12% play both of these sports. If a male student is chosen at random, what is the probability that he plays exactly one of the sports?

    (A) 0.482   (B) 0.55   (C) 0.636   (D) 0.67   (E) 0.79

Answer

4. A confidence interval will be used to estimate a population proportion. If a random sample of size 50 and a random sample of size 200 are selected, and 90% and 95% confidence intervals for the population proportion are calculated for each sample, which of the four confidence intervals is likely to be the narrowest?

(A) The 90% confidence interval for the smaller sample
(B) The 95% confidence interval for the smaller sample
(C) The 90% confidence interval for the larger sample
(D) The 95% confidence interval for the larger sample
(E) The two 95% confidence intervals, they being likely to have roughly equal widths

Answer

5. For a set of 15 decathletes, the correlation between their times for the 100 meter sprint and their distances in the long jump was -0.675. The standard deviation of their 100 meter times was 0.383 seconds and the standard deviation of their long jump distances was 0.469 meters. Denoting 100 meter time by x and long jump distance by y, what is the slope of the least squares regression line of y on x?

(A) -1.012 (B) -0.827 (C) -0.675 (D) -0.551 (E) -0.450

Answer

6. A polling organization is given the job of assessing whether the proportions of homemakers using various types of cooking oil are changing during an advertising campaign. A random sample of homemakers is selected before the campaign starts, and each homemaker in the sample is asked whether he/she primarily uses canola oil, olive oil, sunflower oil, or some other sort of oil for cooking. After the first stage of the campaign, a new random sample of homemakers is selected, and the people selected are asked the same question as those in the first sample. After the final stage of the campaign, a third random sample of homemakers is selected, and the people selected are asked the same question. Which of the following would be most suitable for analysis of the results of this study?

(A) One-sample z-test for a proportion
(B) Two-sample t-test for means
(C) Paired t-test
(D) Chi-square test for goodness of fit
(E) Chi-square test for homogeneity

Answer

7. In an election, the Democratic candidate received 799,072 votes, the Republican candidate received 783,426 votes, and the other two candidates received a combined total of 157,302 votes. These results could be appropriately represented using

(A) a stemplot
(B) a histogram
(C) a pie chart
(D) a boxplot
(E) a scatterplot

Answer

8. It is known that 68% of the adult residents of a large town are male, and that 90% of the adult male residents are employed and 76% of the adult female residents are employed. A random sample of 800 adult residents of the town is selected. Which of the following is closest to the expected number of people in the sample who are employed?

(A) 644   (B) 654   (C) 664   (D) 674   (E) 684

Answer

9. A particular ski slope is used by a large number of people. A researcher wishes to establish whether there is a difference between the mean times taken to complete the descent for men and women. In order to answer this question, independent random samples of men and women using the slope are selected and the times are recorded for the people selected. Let μ_M represent the mean time for all men and let μ_W represent the mean time for all women. If the results of the study are to be analyzed using a hypothesis test, what hypotheses should be used?

(A) $H_0: \mu_M = \mu_W, H_a: \mu_M \neq \mu_W$

(B) $H_0: \mu_M = \mu_W, H_a: \mu_M > \mu_W$

(C) $H_0: \mu_D = 0, H_a: \mu_D \neq 0$

(D) $H_0: \mu_D = 0, H_a: \mu_D > 0$

(E) $H_0: \mu_M > \mu_W, H_a: \mu_M < \mu_W$

Answer

10. Garden Delicious pea pods have lengths that are approximately normally distributed with standard deviation 0.8 inches. The largest 1 percent of pods are eligible for prizes. How many inches above the mean pod length is the smallest pod that is eligible for a prize?

    (A) 1.64   (B) 1.86   (C) 1.94   (D) 2.02   (E) 2.33

    Answer

11. Larry is enrolled in four academic classes. The grades for all the students in Larry's four classes are represented by the boxplots shown below. (The boxplot for the students in Larry's English class shows one outlier, represented by a dot.)

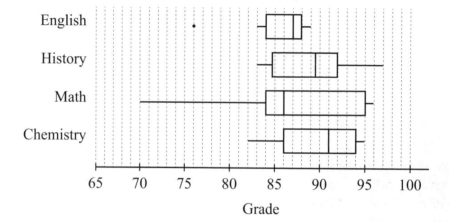

    Larry's grades are 84 in English, 88 in History, 86 in Math, and 92 in Chemistry. His advisor decides to list the four classes according to how well Larry performed relative to his fellow students, with the class in which Larry performed best (relative to his fellow students) showing first in the list. Which of the following is the correct list?

    (A) Chemistry, English, Math, History
    (B) Math, Chemistry, English, History
    (C) Chemistry, Math, English, History
    (D) Math, Chemistry, History, English
    (E) Chemistry, Math, History, English

    Answer

12. A hypothesis test is performed using the results of a random sample from a large population. The test is based on the null hypothesis, H_0, that a population parameter takes a particular value, and the alternative hypothesis, H_a, that the parameter does not take that value. Which of the following is true?

   (A) The results could provide convincing evidence that the null hypothesis is true.
   (B) The results could provide convincing evidence that the alternative hypothesis is true.
   (C) The results could prove that the alternative hypothesis is false.
   (D) The null hypothesis can only be rejected if it is false.
   (E) Failure to reject the null hypothesis means that the null hypothesis is true.

Answer

13. Suppose that it is known that 13% of people are left-handed. If ten people are chosen at random, what is the probability that exactly two of them are left-handed?

   (A) $\frac{1}{10}\binom{10}{2}$

   (B) $(0.13)^2(0.87)^8$

   (C) $(0.87)^2(0.13)^8$

   (D) $\binom{10}{2}(0.13)^2(0.87)^8$

   (E) $\binom{10}{2}(0.87)^2(0.13)^8$

Answer

14. A large Internet-based company serving the USA wishes to send a survey to a sample of its customers. Which of the following will result in a stratified random sample?

    (A) Sending the survey to the next 4000 customers who place orders
    (B) Numbering a complete list of customers sequentially and using a computer to randomly select 4000 customers from the list
    (C) Numbering a complete list of customers sequentially and sending the survey to the customers numbered 258, 1258, 2258, 3258, and so on
    (D) Dividing the country into a large number of regions, randomly selecting 30 of those regions, and sending the survey to all the customers in those 30 regions
    (E) Dividing the customers into four separate groups according to the type of goods primarily ordered, and randomly selecting 1000 customers from each group

Answer

15. For a classroom activity, a teacher uses a bag containing 300 blue chips and 200 red chips. The teacher demonstrates the process of picking ten chips at random from the bag (replacing the chips and mixing between picks) and calculating the proportion of the ten chips that are blue. The students then repeat this process a large number of times, keeping note of the proportion of the ten chips that are blue on each occasion. The standard deviation of all the proportions calculated is likely to be closest to which of the following?

    (A) $\sqrt{\dfrac{(0.6)(0.4)}{10}}$

    (B) $\sqrt{10(0.6)(0.4)}$

    (C) $\sqrt{\dfrac{(0.6)(0.4)}{500}}$

    (D) $\sqrt{500(0.6)(0.4)}$

    (E) $\dfrac{(0.6)(0.4)}{\sqrt{500}}$

Answer

16. A random sample of size 8 has been selected from a large population, and the sample mean, $\bar{x}$, and the sample standard deviation, s, have been calculated. The population standard deviation is unknown. A confidence interval for the population mean is to be constructed. What is the correct formula to use, and what assumption has to be made about the population?

   (A) $\bar{x} \pm z^* \cdot \dfrac{\sigma}{\sqrt{8}}$; no assumption about the about the population is necessary

   (B) $\bar{x} \pm z^* \cdot \dfrac{s}{\sqrt{8}}$; we have to assume that the population is normally distributed

   (C) $\bar{x} \pm t^* \cdot \dfrac{\sigma}{\sqrt{8}}$; no assumption about the about the population is necessary

   (D) $\bar{x} \pm t^* \cdot \dfrac{s}{\sqrt{8}}$; no assumption about the about the population is necessary

   (E) $\bar{x} \pm t^* \cdot \dfrac{s}{\sqrt{8}}$; we have to assume that the population is normally distributed

Answer

17. Frequently, experiments are designed to take account of the fact that many people show improvement resulting purely from the psychological effect of taking tablets, even if the tablets contain no active ingredient.

   In an experiment, the subjects are randomly assigned to two groups. The people in one of the groups (the "treatment group") are given tablets containing a new drug. The people in the other group (the "placebo group") are given tablets that look and taste exactly the same as the other tablets, but contain no active ingredient. In order that the experiment should test the effectiveness of the drug, the experimental design depends on the fact that

   (A) subjects in both groups could experience the potentially positive psychological effect of taking tablets
   (B) only subjects in the placebo group could experience the potentially positive psychological effect of taking tablets
   (C) only subjects in the treatment group could experience the potentially positive psychological effect of taking tablets
   (D) no subject in the experiment will experience the potentially positive psychological effect of taking tablets
   (E) nobody could ever experience a positive psychological effect as a result of taking tablets

Answer

Questions 18 and 19 refer to the following scenario and numerical information.

Eighty runners took part in a cross country race. Their times are summarized in the table below.

Time (minutes)	16	18	20	22	24	26	28	30	32
Cumulative Relative Frequency	0.000	0.0750	0.2625	0.5125	0.7125	0.8250	0.9375	0.9750	1.000

(The cumulative relative frequencies refer to the proportions of runners whose times were less than or equal to the times given.)

18. How many runners had times that were more than 20 minutes and at most 22 minutes?

    (A) 10   (B) 20   (C) 30   (D) 40   (E) 50

Answer

19. Which of the following could be the interquartile range of the times?

    (A) 3 minutes, 50 seconds
    (B) 4 minutes, 40 seconds
    (C) 8 minutes, 20 seconds
    (D) 10 minutes, 30 seconds
    (E) 12 minutes, 10 seconds

Answer

20. A random sample of 50 Brand A light bulbs and an independent random sample of 45 Brand B light bulbs were selected, and the lives (in hours) of the bulbs in the samples were measured. The partial computer output below shows the results of a test of H_0: $\mu_A = \mu_B$ versus H_a: $\mu_A \neq \mu_B$.

```
Two-sample T for Brand A vs Brand B

            N      Mean        StDev       SE Mean
Brand A    50     907.6        60.2         8.5
Brand B    45     890.8        46.0         6.9

Difference = mu (Brand A) - mu (Brand B)

T-Test of difference = 0 (vs not =):
T-Value = 1.54     P-Value = 0.127     DF = 90
```

Which of the following is NOT true?

(A) H_0 is not rejected at the 0.05 significance level.
(B) The value 1.54 is less than the positive critical value of a t distribution with 90 degrees of freedom for a single-tail probability of 0.025.
(C) A 95% two-sample t confidence interval based on these results would contain zero.
(D) If the population means were equal, the probability of getting a t statistic whose absolute value is at least 1.54 would be 0.127.
(E) Given a difference in sample means of 16.8, the probability that the population means are equal is 0.127.

Answer

21. Three statistics, Statistic 1, Statistic 2, and Statistic 3, are to be compared as estimators of a particular population parameter. To estimate the behavior of the statistics, 600 random samples are selected from the population, and the value of each statistic is calculated for each sample. The true value of the population parameter is 5. The distributions of the values of the three statistics are shown in the graphs below.

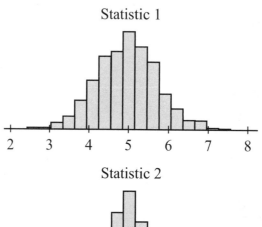

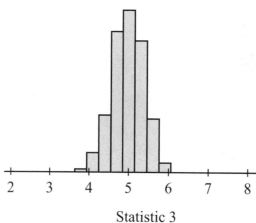

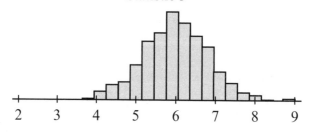

The three statistics are to be listed in order of preference, with the best statistic first in the list. Which of the following is correct?

(A) 1, 2, 3   (B) 2, 1, 3   (C) 1, 3, 2   (D) 3, 1, 2   (E) 2, 3, 1

Answer

22. A simple random sample of size 50 is selected from a population, and a measurement is taken for each individual in the sample. These results will be used to test the null hypothesis H_0: $\mu = 8$ *versus* the alternative hypothesis H_a: $\mu > 8$. A significance level of $\alpha = 0.05$ will be used for the test. Assuming that the true value of the population mean, μ, is greater than 8, which of the following would produce a test that has greater power than the one given above?

    I. Changing the significance level to $\alpha = 0.1$
   II. Changing the alternative hypothesis to H_a: $\mu \neq 8$
  III. Increasing the sample size to 100

(A) I only   (B) II only   (C) III only   (D) I and III   (E) II and III

Answer

23. A survey is to be designed in order to estimate some quantities associated with a population. Which of the following is NOT true?

(A) A census will always be more representative of the population than a sample.
(B) How well a sample will represent the population is influenced by the quality of the sampling method used.
(C) How well a random sample will represent the population is partly a matter of chance.
(D) A simple random sample will always represent the population better than a systematic sample.
(E) A convenience sample is unlikely to be representative of the population.

Answer

24. In a particular state, it is known that 40% of daily trips are for shopping or running errands, 30% are for social or recreational purposes, 18% are for commuting to work, and 12% are for other purposes. A survey in one town within the state included 500 daily trips, of which 192 were for shopping or running errands, 133 were for social or recreational purposes, 118 were for commuting to work, and 57 were for other purposes. A hypothesis test is conducted in order to find out whether the pattern of daily trips for the town differs from the pattern for the state as a whole. (The test is based on the assumption that the 500 daily trips in the survey form a random sample of the daily trips for the town.) What is the value of the test statistic?

(A) 1.59   (B) 5.03   (C) 8.23   (D) 9.31   (E) 11.11

Answer

25. It is known that one-fifth of the vehicles that pass a particular intersection are commercial vehicles, and that the vehicles pass this intersection independently. A student is planning to stand at the intersection and count the vehicles that pass up to and including the first commercial vehicle. Which of the following best describes the distribution of the number of vehicles the student will count?

(A) Binomial
(B) Chi-square
(C) Geometric
(D) Normal
(E) t

Answer

26. The management of a factory wishes to compare a new machine for producing saucers with the machine the factory currently uses for that purpose. Random samples of 80 saucers from the new machine and 100 saucers from the current machine are selected, and it is found that 17 of the saucers from the new machine and 28 of the saucers from the current machine have faults. The new machine will be incorporated if, and only if, these results provide convincing evidence at the 0.05 significance level that the proportion of faulty saucers is less for the new machine than for the current machine. Will the new machine be incorporated?

(A) Yes, because $P\left(z < \dfrac{0.2125 - 0.28}{\sqrt{\dfrac{(0.2125)(0.7875)}{80} + \dfrac{(0.28)(0.72)}{100}}}\right)$ is greater than 0.05.

(B) No, because $P\left(z < \dfrac{0.2125 - 0.28}{\sqrt{\dfrac{(0.2125)(0.7875)}{80} + \dfrac{(0.28)(0.72)}{100}}}\right)$ is greater than 0.05.

(C) Yes, because $P\left(z < \dfrac{0.2125 - 0.28}{\sqrt{(0.25)(0.75)\left(\dfrac{1}{80} + \dfrac{1}{100}\right)}}\right)$ is greater than 0.05.

(D) No, because $P\left(z < \dfrac{0.2125 - 0.28}{\sqrt{(0.25)(0.75)\left(\dfrac{1}{80} + \dfrac{1}{100}\right)}}\right)$ is greater than 0.05.

(E) Yes, because $P\left(z < \dfrac{0.2125 - 0.28}{\sqrt{(0.25)(0.75)\left(\dfrac{1}{80} + \dfrac{1}{100}\right)}}\right)$ is less than 0.05.

Answer

Questions 27 and 28 refer to the following scenario and numerical information.

The department of transportation for a particular state kept records of the number of new cars sold (x) and the number of used cars sold (y) for each month last year. Some computer output from a regression analysis of these data is shown below.

```
Dependent variable: Number of used cars sold

Predictor    Coef       StDev      T       P
Constant     32971      9656       3.41    0.007
New_cars     0.8566     0.4593     1.86    0.092

S = 5418.57      R-Sq = 25.8%      R-Sq(adj) = 18.4%
```

27. During the month of July, 22,836 new cars and 57,693 used cars were sold. What is the residual for this data point?

    (A) 5161   (B) −5161   (C) 5323   (D) −5323   (E) −5774

    Answer

28. Treating the twelve months last year as a random sample of all months, and assuming that the other conditions for inference are met, at what level of significance do last year's results provide evidence of a non-zero slope in the population regression line of y on x?

    (A) At the 0.01 level
    (B) At the 0.05 level, but not at the 0.01 level
    (C) At the 0.1 level, but not at the 0.05 level
    (D) At the 0.05 level, but not at the 0.1 level
    (E) Not at any reasonable significance level

    Answer

29. Which of the following could be conducted in a double-blind manner?

    (A) An experiment to investigate whether listening to music while typing increases the number of errors made
    (B) An experiment to investigate whether regular exercise reduces blood pressure
    (C) An experiment to investigate whether taking vitamin C speeds recovery from a cold
    (D) An experiment to investigate whether drinking sufficient quantities of water increases the effectiveness of food supplements
    (E) An experiment to investigate whether use of keyboard shortcuts reduces the time taken to perform a particular computer task

Answer

30. A transportation authority conducts a survey of users of a commuter railroad. A random sample of passengers is selected, and each passenger in the sample is given a questionnaire. There are two questions on the questionnaire. The first question asks whether the passenger paid for the journey at the ticket office, using a machine located on the platform, or online. The second question asks how happy the passenger is with the transportation service (very happy, happy, neutral, or unhappy). A hypothesis test will be conducted to determine whether there is an association between the method of payment and happiness with the service. The test will use a chi-square distribution with k degrees of freedom. What is the value of k?

    (A) 2 (B) 3 (C) 6 (D) 9 (E) 12

Answer

31. After a successful year, a company decides to increase the salaries of all of its employees by 5 percent. Which of the following will NOT be increased by 5 percent?

    (A) The mean salary
    (B) The standard deviation of the salaries
    (C) The variance of the salaries
    (D) The median salary
    (E) The interquartile range of the salaries

Answer

32. An experiment is to be designed to compare the side-effects associated with a new drug with those associated with a current drug designed for the same purpose. It is accepted that the older a person is, the more likely it is that the person will be negatively affected by these drugs. The designers of the experiment therefore decide to block by age. This blocking will ensure that

    (A) all the older people will receive one of the drugs, with the younger people receiving the other drug
    (B) in terms of age, the people who receive the new drug are different from the people who receive the current drug
    (C) in terms of age, the people who receive the new drug are similar to the people who receive the current drug
    (D) the people who take the current drug will be similar to each other with respect to age, and the people who take the new drug will be similar to each other with respect to age
    (E) the assignment of the subjects to the two drugs is completely random

Answer

33. In the context of linear regression, an influential point is a data point whose removal would have a large effect on the least squares regression line of y on x. For reasonably large data sets, which of the following are true?

    I. Any point with a large residual is an influential point.
   II. Any point that is an outlier in the x-direction is an influential point.
  III. Removal of an influential point could increase the absolute value of the correlation coefficient.

  (A) II only
  (B) III only
  (C) I and II only
  (D) II and III only
  (E) I, II, and III

Answer

34. It is estimated that, for the people in a large community, the standard deviation of the daily calorie intake is 245. Assuming that this standard deviation is correct, how large a random sample of people from the community would be necessary in order to estimate the mean daily calorie intake to within 30 calories with 95% confidence?

  (A) 17   (B) 131   (C) 257   (D) 308   (E) 3922

Answer

35. Two blue cubes and three green cubes, each with faces labeled 1–6, will be rolled. Letting X be the total score for the two blue cubes and Y be the total score for the three green cubes, it can be shown that the standard deviations of the random variables X and Y are 2.42 and 2.96, respectively. Which of the following is the standard deviation of $X - Y$?

(A) −2.91   (B) −0.54   (C) 3.82   (D) 4.68   (E) 14.62

Answer

36. A statistics question requires a significance test with null hypothesis H_0: $p = 0.3$, where p is a population proportion. Two students, Juan and Tamara, both do the question, and they both calculate the correct positive value of the z-statistic. However, Juan performs a one-tailed test (using the alternative hypothesis H_a: $p > 0.3$), and Tamara performs a two-tailed test (using the alternative hypothesis H_a: $p \neq 0.3$). Given that both students are correct in their work, which of the following is NOT possible?

(A) Both students reject the null hypothesis at the 0.05 significance level.
(B) Both students fail to reject the null hypothesis at the 0.05 significance level.
(C) Juan rejects the null hypothesis at the 0.05 significance level and Tamara fails to reject the null hypothesis at the 0.05 significance level.
(D) Juan fails to reject the null hypothesis at the 0.05 significance level and Tamara rejects the null hypothesis at the 0.05 significance level.
(E) Juan fails to reject the null hypothesis at the 0.01 significance level and Tamara rejects the null hypothesis at the 0.05 significance level.

Answer

37. A random sample will be selected from a population of rabbits. The weights of the rabbits in the sample will be measured, and the sample mean weight will be calculated. Assuming that the sample size is greater than 1, the standard deviation of the sampling distribution of the sample mean is

    (A) less than the population standard deviation, because the weight of any rabbit in the sample is likely to be closer to the population mean than the weight of a rabbit chosen at random from the population
    (B) less than the population standard deviation, because, when calculating the sample mean, weights in the sample far from the population mean are averaged out with the other weights in the sample
    (C) equal to the population standard deviation
    (D) more than the population standard deviation, because there is a greater possibility of getting a weight that is far from the population mean in the sample than when picking one rabbit at random
    (E) more than the population standard deviation, because using a large sample introduces a greater possibility of the sample mean being far from the population mean

    Answer

38. A statistics teacher calculates the correlation between the heights (in inches) and the weights (in pounds) of the students in her class. Which of the following would change the value of the correlation coefficient?

    (A) Adding 5 inches to each height
    (B) Subtracting 10 pounds from each weight
    (C) Adding 5 inches to each height and subtracting 10 pounds from each weight
    (D) Subtracting each height from 100
    (E) Converting the heights to centimeters

    Answer

39. An article describes a *t*-test of $H_0: \mu = 20$ *versus* $H_a: \mu > 20$, and the value of the test statistic is given to be 1.58. The sample size is not given in the article, but is known to be between 5 and 30 inclusive. Assuming that all the conditions for inference are met, the *p*-value for the test would be

    (A) less than 0.01
    (B) between 0.01 and 0.05
    (C) between 0.05 and 0.1
    (D) between 0.1 and 0.2
    (E) greater than 0.2

Answer

40. The ethnic breakdown of a particular county is known to be as follows: Caucasian: 38%, Hispanic: 34%, African American: 16%, and Asian: 12%. If two people are chosen at random from this county, what is the approximate probability that they are of the same ethnicity? (The population of the county can be assumed to be large.)

    (A) 0.28   (B) 0.30   (C) 0.32   (D) 0.34   (E) 0.36

Answer

SECTION II
Part A
Questions 1–5
Spend about 65 minutes on this part of the exam.
Percent of Section II grade—75

Directions: Show all your work. Indicate clearly the methods you use, because you will be graded on the correctness of your method as well as on the accuracy and completeness of your results and explanations.

1. The graphical display below shows the proportions of male and female students in the undergraduate, master's, and doctoral programs at a particular university. These are the only three programs available at this university.

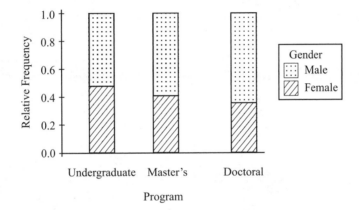

(a) What does the display reveal about the way the gender balance varies between the three programs?

(b) Does the information in the display imply that the number of males in the doctoral program is greater than the number of males in the masters program? Explain.

(c) When selecting a student at random from the university, are the events "is enrolled in the doctoral program" and "is female" mutually exclusive? Justify your answer.

(d) When selecting a student at random from the university, are the events "is enrolled in the doctoral program" and "is female" independent? Justify your answer.

2. A study concluded that AP students who attend extra study sessions do better, on average, on their AP exams than students who do not attend extra study sessions.

(a) Explain why we cannot conclude from the result of the study that attending extra study sessions *causes* increased AP scores. Include an example of a plausible confounding variable.

An experiment is designed where 200 AP students will be randomly assigned to two groups (Group A and Group B), each of size 100. The students in Group A will be required to attend extra study sessions, while those in Group B will not be given that opportunity.

(b) Explain how the 200 students might be randomly assigned to the two treatment groups.

(c) Suppose that the students in Group A receive significantly higher AP results, on average, than the students in Group B. Explain why we now *do* have evidence that attending extra study sessions increases AP scores.

3. For every household in a particular county, the water use (in thousands of gallons) over the course of a year was recorded. The mean water use for the households in the county was found to be 162 and the standard deviation was 140.

(a) Based on the information given above, could the distribution of household water use for that county be approximately normal? Explain your answer.

(b) A random sample of 50 households will be selected, and the mean water use will be calculated for the households in the sample. Is the sampling distribution of the sample mean for random samples of size 50 approximately normal? Explain.

(c) Suppose that the annual indoor water use (in thousands of gallons) for the same county is approximately normally distributed with mean 57 and standard deviation 12. If a random sample of 50 households is selected, what is the probability that their mean indoor water use (in thousands of gallons) will be greater than 59?

4. Random samples of 48 girls and 45 boys were selected from a large school district. It was found that 37 of the girls and 20 of the boys were not consuming the recommended amount of vitamin A.

   (a) Use a 95% confidence interval to estimate the difference between the proportions of girls and boys in the school district who do not consume the recommended amount of vitamin A.

   (b) Based only on this confidence interval, do you think that there is a difference between the proportions of girls and boys in the district who are not consuming the recommended amount of vitamin A? Justify your answer.

5. Exposure of workers to asbestos at construction sites and shipyards is considered dangerous. The workers at a construction site are concerned that asbestos might be present in the air, and so an inspector has been called. The inspector will select a random sample of locations at the site and will measure the asbestos level at those locations. If the data collected by the inspector provide convincing evidence that mean level of asbestos at the site is below the permissible exposure limit of 0.1 fibers per cubic centimeter (f/cc) then work at the site will be allowed to continue. Otherwise, work will stop until precautions have been put into place.

(a) The results of the inspection will be analyzed by means of a hypothesis test. State the null and alternative hypotheses that would be used for the test, and define the parameter of interest.

(b) In the context of this situation, describe Type I and Type II errors and describe the consequences for the workers of each type of error.

SECTION II
Part B
Question 6
Spend about 25 minutes on this part of the exam.
Percent of Section II grade—25

Directions: Show all your work. Indicate clearly the methods you use, because you will be graded on the correctness of your method as well as on the accuracy and completeness of your results and explanations.

6. A meteorological organization records the daily temperatures at noon (local time) at various locations across the world. A time plot for the temperatures at Location A last year is shown below. (The days of the year are numbered 1 through 365, with "1" representing January 1st, and "365" representing December 31st. The days are shown on the horizontal axis, and, for each day, a single point is plotted showing the temperature for that day.) Additionally, a histogram summarizing the Location A temperatures for the same year is provided.

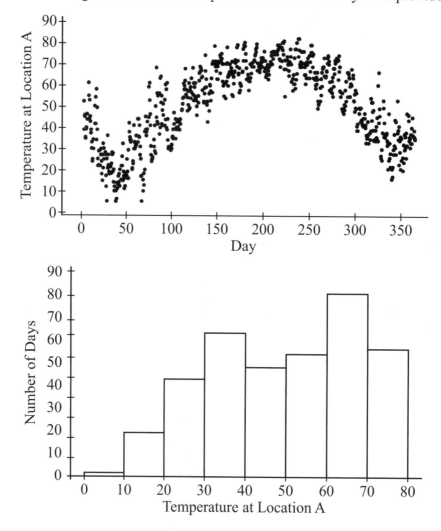

104

(a) Give two facts that are obvious from the histogram but are not obvious from the time plot.

(b) Give one fact that is obvious from the time plot but is not obvious from the histogram.

A time plot showing the temperatures at a different location, Location B, during the same year is shown below.

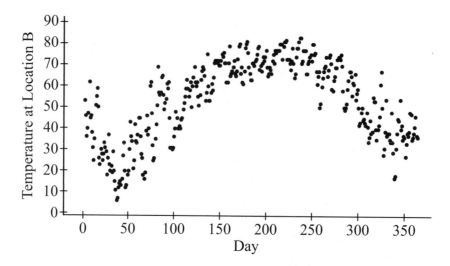

(c) A scatterplot will be constructed where, for each day in the given year, the temperature at Location A will be plotted as the *x*-coordinate and the temperature at Location B will be plotted as the *y*-coordinate. Make a rough sketch as to what the appearance of this scatterplot would be. Include approximate scales on your axes, but do not attempt to plot points exactly.

(d) Locations A and B are close geographically. A researcher wishes to establish whether, on average, the temperature at Location B is higher than at Location A. The researcher is willing to treat the days in the year considered above as a random sample of all days at the two locations. Name a hypothesis test that would be appropriate for answering the researcher's question.

The scatterplot below summarizes the temperatures at Location A and at a new location, Location C, for the days of the same year.

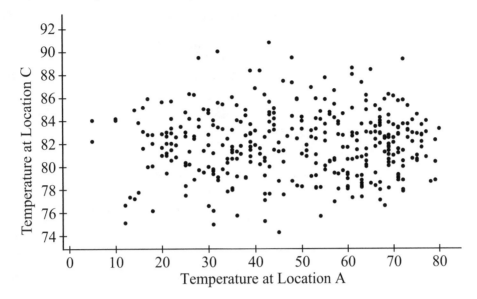

(e) Make a rough sketch of a possible appearance of the time plot for the temperatures at Location C during that same year. Include rough scales for your axes, but do not attempt to plot points exactly.

Sample Examination Two

SECTION I
Time—1 hour and 30 minutes
Number of questions—40
Percent of total grade—50

Directions: Solve each of the following problems, using the available space for scratch work. Decide which is the best of the choices given and fill in the corresponding oval on the answer sheet. No credit will be given for anything written in the test book. Do not spend too much time on any one problem.

---

1. The dotplot below shows the number of goals scored by the Gator Girls soccer team in their games last year.

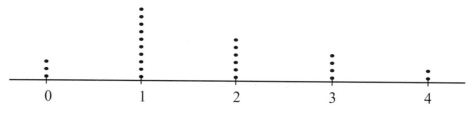

Number of Goals Scored

Which of the following could be used to compute the mean number of goals scored per game?

(A) $\dfrac{1+2}{2}$

(B) $\dfrac{0+1+2+3+4}{5}$

(C) $\dfrac{3+10+6+4+2}{5}$

(D) $\dfrac{3\cdot0+10\cdot1+6\cdot2+4\cdot3+2\cdot4}{5}$

(E) $\dfrac{3\cdot0+10\cdot1+6\cdot2+4\cdot3+2\cdot4}{3+10+6+4+2}$

Answer

108

2. There is concern that carrying weights while walking could increase the walker's blood pressure. In order to investigate this, an experiment is designed that will use a set of college student volunteers. None of the students has engaged in regular exercise prior to the experiment, and all of the students are willing to walk every day during the course of the experiment. By random assignment it is determined for each participant whether the person will carry in each hand weights of 2 pounds, 4 pounds, 6 pounds, or no weights at all, and also whether the person will walk 2 miles each day or 4 miles each day. The number of treatments used in this experiment is

(A) 1   (B) 2   (C) 4   (D) 6   (E) 8

Answer

3. In which of the following hypothesis tests could a *t*-distribution be the most appropriate distribution to use for calculation of the *p*-value?

(A) A test for a population mean where the population standard deviation is known
(B) A test for a population mean where the population standard deviation is unknown
(C) A test for a population proportion
(D) A goodness of fit test
(E) A test for independence of two categorical variables

Answer

4. Three brothers are arguing as to which of them did best in their end-of-year math exams. Robert, who is in the 10th grade, got an 84. Justin, who is in the 8th grade, got a 93. Bryan, who is in the 7th grade, got an 81. In order to sort out the argument, their mother suggests they ask their teachers what the overall means and standard deviations were for each of the exams. These quantities, along with the brothers' scores, are given in the table below.

	Score	Exam Mean	Exam Standard Deviation
Robert	84	77.1	7.3
Justin	93	82.0	7.8
Bryan	81	73.2	6.9

Using this information, the brothers decide which of them did best, which did second best, and which did third best, relative to their fellow students. Which of the following is the correct list (with the brother who did best relative to his fellow students first in the list)?

(A) Robert, Justin, Bryan
(B) Robert, Bryan, Justin
(C) Justin, Robert, Bryan
(D) Justin, Bryan, Robert
(E) Bryan, Robert, Justin

Answer

5. A large two-year college has found that the number of years completed by the population of students attending the college has the distribution given in the table below.

Number of Years Completed	0	1	2
Proportion of Students	0.08	0.22	0.70

(This tells us that 8% of students attending the college do not complete their first year, 22% complete their first year but not their second year, and the remaining 70% complete the entire two-year program.)

It can be calculated, using the information in the table, that the mean number of years completed for students attending this college is 1.62. Which of the following is the standard deviation of the number of years completed by students attending this college?

(A) $\sqrt{(0-1.62)^2 + (1-1.62)^2 + (2-1.62)^2}$

(B) $\sqrt{(0-1.62)^2(0.08) + (1-1.62)^2(0.22) + (2-1.62)^2(0.70)}$

(C) $\sqrt{\dfrac{(0-1.62)^2 + (1-1.62)^2 + (2-1.62)^2}{2}}$

(D) $\sqrt{\dfrac{(0-1.62)^2 + (1-1.62)^2 + (2-1.62)^2}{3}}$

(E) $\sqrt{\dfrac{(0-1.62)^2(0.08) + (1-1.62)^2(0.22) + (2-1.62)^2(0.70)}{3}}$

Answer

6. A researcher wishes to find out whether ducks of a particular breed tend to lay more eggs in the summer than in the winter. The researcher selects a random sample of ducks of this breed, and, over the course of a year, notes for each duck in the sample the number of eggs laid in the summer and the number of eggs laid in the winter. Which of the following would be a suitable test for analyzing the results of this study?

   (A) One-sample z-test for a mean
   (B) Two-sample t-test for means
   (C) Paired t-test
   (D) One-proportion z-test
   (E) Two-proportion z-test

Answer

7. A large population has mean μ and standard deviation σ. A random sample of size n will be taken from the population. The Central Limit Theorem tells us that

   (A) the mean of the sampling distribution of the sample mean is μ

   (B) the standard deviation of the sampling distribution of the sample mean is $\dfrac{\sigma}{\sqrt{n}}$

   (C) if n is large, the sampling distribution of the sample mean is approximately normal

   (D) since the population is large, the sampling distribution of the sample mean must be approximately normal

   (E) the standard deviation of the sampling distribution of the sample mean is greater than the standard deviation of the population

Answer

8. In a pilot study, a random sample of 98 adults is selected from a large town, and it is found that 33 of these 98 people consume vegetables three or more times per day. A one-proportion z-test is used to analyze this result. According to the test, does this sample result provide convincing evidence at a 5 percent level of significance that more than 25 percent of the adults in the town consume vegetables three or more times per day?

   (A) Yes, since the test statistic is less than the critical value.
   (B) Yes, since the test statistic is greater than the critical value.
   (C) No, since the test statistic is less than the critical value.
   (D) No, since the test statistic is greater than the critical value.
   (E) The question cannot be answered, since the sample was not large enough for a one-proportion z-test to be used.

   Answer

9. For two events A and B, let $P(A \mid B)$ denote the conditional probability that A occurs given that B occurs, and let $P(B \mid A)$ denote the conditional probability that B occurs given that A occurs. If $P(A \text{ and } B) \neq 0$, and $P(A \mid B) = P(B \mid A)$, which of the following must be true?

   (A) A and B are independent.
   (B) A and B are mutually exclusive.
   (C) A and B have equal probabilities.
   (D) The sum of the probabilities of A and B is 1.
   (E) $P(A \mid B)$ and $P(B \mid A)$ are both equal to 1.

   Answer

10.

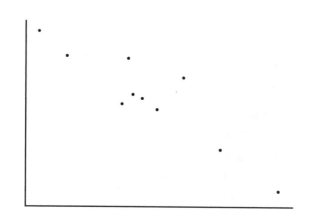

Which of the following could be the value of the correlation coefficient for the data set represented by the scatterplot above?

(A) -0.91 (B) -0.34 (C) 0.03 (D) 0.34 (E) 0.91

Answer

11. Following an oil spill, a particular region of the ocean is being tested for the level of a chemical called naphthalene. It is considered fact that fish from the region will be safe to eat if, and only if, the mean naphthalene level in the region is less than 3.3 parts per billion. A set of water specimens will be randomly selected from the region and tested, and if the results provide convincing evidence that the mean naphthalene level is less than 3.3, then the sale of fish from the region will be made legal. Which of the following describes a Type I error and its consequences?

(A) The authorities obtain convincing evidence that the mean naphthalene level is less than 3.3, and legalize the sale of fish that are in fact <u>safe</u> for consumption.
(B) The authorities obtain convincing evidence that the mean naphthalene level is less than 3.3, and legalize the sale of fish that are in fact <u>unsafe</u> for consumption.
(C) The authorities fail to obtain convincing evidence that the mean naphthalene level is less than 3.3, and do not legalize the sale of fish from the region when in fact the fish are <u>safe</u> for consumption.
(D) The authorities fail to obtain convincing evidence that the mean naphthalene level is less than 3.3, and do not legalize the sale of fish from the region when in fact the fish are <u>unsafe</u> for consumption.
(E) The definition of a Type I error depends on the actual results of the study in question.

Answer

12. The cumulative relative frequency plot shown below summarizes the family earnings (expressed in US dollars) in a particular country. (The earnings of each family were expressed to the nearest dollar, and the cumulative relative frequencies in the graph indicate the proportions of families earning less than or equal to the amounts shown on the horizontal axis.)

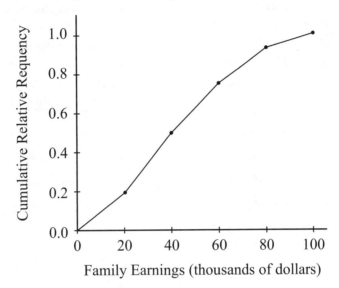

Family Earnings (thousands of dollars)

Which of the income brackets below contains the most families?

(A) $0 to $20,000
(B) $20,001 to $40,000
(C) $40,001 to $60,000
(D) $60,001 to $80,000
(E) $80,001 to $100,000

Answer

Questions 13 and 14 refer to the following scenario.

When a person watches a movie, does the video quality (how good the picture and sound are) make any difference as to how high the person rates the content of the movie? Suppose that 90 male college students are shown the same movie, watching in separate locations. By random assignment, 40 of the students are shown the movie in low video quality, with the other 50 students being shown the movie in high video quality. Each student is asked to rate the content of the movie as "Bad," "OK," or "Awesome." The results are shown in the table below.

		Rating of Content Quality			
		"Bad"	"OK"	"Awesome"	Total
Video Quality	Low	15	11	14	40
	High	14	12	24	50
	Total	29	23	38	90

A chi-square test for homogeneity will be used to analyze these results. The expected counts required for the test are shown in the table below.

		Rating of Content Quality			
		"Bad"	"OK"	"Awesome"	Total
Video Quality	Low	12.89	10.22	16.89	40
	High	16.11	12.78	21.11	50
	Total	29	23	38	90

13. Which of the following could be used to calculate the chi-square statistic for this hypothesis test?

(A) $\dfrac{40 \cdot 29}{90} + \dfrac{40 \cdot 23}{90} + \dfrac{40 \cdot 38}{90} + \dfrac{50 \cdot 29}{90} + \dfrac{50 \cdot 23}{90} + \dfrac{50 \cdot 38}{90}$

(B) $\dfrac{15 - 12.89}{15} + \dfrac{11 - 10.22}{11} + \dfrac{14 - 16.89}{14} + \dfrac{14 - 16.11}{14} + \dfrac{12 - 12.78}{12} + \dfrac{24 - 21.11}{24}$

(C) $\dfrac{|15 - 12.89|}{12.89} + \dfrac{|11 - 10.22|}{10.22} + \dfrac{|14 - 16.89|}{16.89} + \dfrac{|14 - 16.11|}{16.11} + \dfrac{|12 - 12.78|}{12.78} + \dfrac{|24 - 21.11|}{21.11}$

(D) $\dfrac{(15 - 12.89)^2}{15} + \dfrac{(11 - 10.22)^2}{11} + \dfrac{(14 - 16.89)^2}{14} + \dfrac{(14 - 16.11)^2}{14} + \dfrac{(12 - 12.78)^2}{12}$
$+ \dfrac{(24 - 21.11)^2}{24}$

(E) $\dfrac{(15 - 12.89)^2}{12.89} + \dfrac{(11 - 10.22)^2}{10.22} + \dfrac{(14 - 16.89)^2}{16.89} + \dfrac{(14 - 16.11)^2}{16.11} + \dfrac{(12 - 12.78)^2}{12.78}$
$+ \dfrac{(24 - 21.11)^2}{21.11}$

Answer

14. Of the following, which is closest to the true meaning of the *p*-value for this hypothesis test?

(A) The probability of getting observed counts that are at least as far from the expected counts as was the case in this study given that video quality has no effect on the rating of content quality

(B) The probability of getting observed counts that are at least as far from the expected counts as was the case in this study given that video quality has an effect on the rating of content quality

(C) The probability of getting the observed counts that were obtained in this study given that video quality has an effect on the rating of content quality

(D) The probability that video quality has no effect on the rating of content quality given the results that were obtained in this study

(E) The probability that video quality has an effect on the rating of content quality given the results that were obtained in this study

Answer

15. Tammi's high school consists of 840 students in grades 9-12. Tammi will select a simple random sample of 20 students from the school. Which of the following is NOT true?

(A) This could be achieved by printing the names of all 840 students on identical slips of paper, placing the slips in a large container, picking out 20 slips at random, and including in the sample the 20 students whose names are picked.

(B) This could be achieved by obtaining a list of the 840 students, assigning a distinct random 10-digit number to each student, sorting the list by the size of the random number, and including in the sample the first 20 names on the sorted list.

(C) Any subset of size 20 of the students at the school will have the same probability of being the sample that Tammi selects.

(D) Any student at the school will have the same probability of appearing in the sample.

(E) Tammi's method will ensure that there is an adequate representation of all four grades in the sample.

Answer

16. Which of the following is most likely to be approximately normally distributed?

    (A) The scores on a very easy 5-question mental math quiz taken by a large number of students
    (B) The scores on a large number of rolls of a cube whose faces are numbered 1 through 6
    (C) The number of attempts it took to pass the drivers' test for the population of drivers in New York State
    (D) The tail lengths of fully grown males of the common raccoon species
    (E) The responses to a survey question given to a large number of people where the possible responses were "yes," "no," and "maybe"

Answer

17. A federation of play-based nursery and elementary schools has found, in the children at its schools, a correlation of 0.65 between time spent playing with brick-based construction toys in nursery school (in minutes per day) and first grade math score (on a scale of 0 to 100). Which of the following is implied by this information?

    (A) Playing with brick-based construction toys in nursery school causes an increase in first grade math score.
    (B) If the time spent playing with brick-based construction toys had been recorded in hours per day instead of minutes per day, then the correlation would have been 0.65/60.
    (C) When time spent playing with brick-based construction toys (in minutes per day) increases by 1, the average increase in first grade math score is 0.65.
    (D) If two children are selected from those included in the study, then the one with the greater time spent playing with brick-based construction toys will have the higher first grade math score.
    (E) Less than half of the variation in first grade math score can be explained by the regression line of first grade math score on time spent playing with brick-based construction toys in nursery school.

Answer

18. When an experiment is intended to compare two or more treatments, a good design <u>must</u>

    (A) include a control group
    (B) include some random assignment to treatments
    (C) include a group that receives a placebo
    (D) involve some sort of blocking
    (E) be double blind

Answer

19. Which of the following is true?

    I. In a t-test for a single population mean, increasing the sample size (while leaving everything else the same) changes the number of degrees of freedom used in the test.
    II. In a chi-square test for independence, increasing the sample size (while leaving everything else the same) changes the number of degrees of freedom used in the test.
    III. In a t-test for the slope of the population regression line, increasing the number of observations (while leaving everything else the same) changes the number of degrees of freedom used in the test.

    (A) I only
    (B) I and II only
    (C) I and III only
    (D) II and III only
    (E) I, II and III

Answer

20. The boxplot below represents a data set with one outlier.

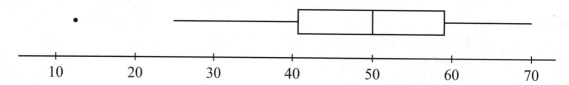

If the outlier were to be removed, what would happen to the mean and the standard deviation of the data set?

(A) Both the mean and the standard deviation would remain the same.
(B) Both the mean and the standard deviation would increase.
(C) Both the mean and the standard deviation would decrease.
(D) The mean would increase and the standard deviation would decrease.
(E) The mean would decrease and the standard deviation would increase.

Answer

21. A town has recently moved over to single stream recycling, an approach to waste disposal that recycles a far greater proportion of household refuse than the town's previous approach. Local administrators are interested in determining the degree to which the new approach is being adopted by households in the town. Of the following, which would be likely to produce the most accurate answer to the administrators' question?

(A) Placing researchers at the town's Whole Nutrition food market, and having the researchers select customers of varying genders and ethnicities. The researchers ask the people to state whether they "strongly agree," "agree," "have no opinion," "disagree" or "strongly disagree" with the statement: "My household has substantially changed its approach to refuse disposal as a result of the town's recent change."

(B) Placing researchers at the town's railroad station, bus terminal, mall, and supermarkets, and having the researchers select people of varying genders, ethnicities, and socioeconomic backgrounds. The researchers ask the people to state whether they "strongly agree," "agree," "have no opinion," "disagree" or "strongly disagree" with the statement: "My household has substantially changed its approach to refuse disposal as a result of the town's policies of improving the environment by recycling greater proportions of household waste."

(C) Selecting a large random sample from a complete list of households. Telephone or visit the households selected (repeatedly returning until a response is obtained) asking an adult to state whether he/she "strongly agrees," "agrees," "has no opinion," "disagrees" or "strongly disagrees" with the statement: "My household has substantially changed its approach to refuse disposal as a result of the town's recent change."

(D) Placing leaflets in the mailboxes of all the households in the town asking an adult from the household to respond online to a survey. The online survey asks people to state whether they "strongly agree," "agree," "have no opinion," "disagree" or "strongly disagree" with the statement: "My household has substantially changed its approach to refuse disposal as a result of the town's recent change."

(E) Scheduling a phone-in program on the local radio station that discusses people's feelings and impressions regarding the town's recent change of policy.

Answer

22. Let the proportion of houses in a large city that have mold in their basements be p. When a random sample of n houses is selected from the city, which of the following is the standard deviation of the sampling distribution of $\hat{p}$, the proportion of houses in the sample that have mold in their basements?

   (A) $\sqrt{\dfrac{p(1-p)}{n}}$

   (B) $\sqrt{\dfrac{\hat{p}(1-\hat{p})}{n}}$

   (C) $\dfrac{\hat{p}(1-\hat{p})}{n}$

   (D) $\sqrt{np(1-p)}$

   (E) $\sqrt{n\hat{p}(1-\hat{p})}$

   Answer

23. Jimmy, a very promising 8th grader, is taking an AP Statistics class. The teacher has generated on a computer a large set of numbers that are approximately normally distributed and are being considered as the population. Each student is asked to select a random sample from the population and use the sample to construct a 95% confidence interval for the population mean. Jimmy goes ahead and does this. However, when the teacher announces the true population mean to the class, Jimmy notices that the population mean does not lie within his confidence interval. Which of the following is true?

   (A) Jimmy's work could have been correct. Confidence intervals are designed to be narrow, and therefore, for most random samples, the population parameter being estimated will not lie within the interval.
   (B) Jimmy's work could have been correct. For about 5% of students doing this exercise correctly the population mean will not lie within the confidence interval calculated.
   (C) Jimmy's work could have been correct. It will always be the case that the population mean is not within the confidence interval when the population mean doesn't happen to be in the sample selected.
   (D) There must be an error in Jimmy's work. The whole point of confidence intervals is that they should capture the population parameter that is being estimated.
   (E) There must be an error in Jimmy's work. He must have calculated an interval that was too narrow, and it was this that caused the interval not to capture the population mean.

   Answer

24. Suppose that a detailed study has revealed that for romance novels the number of pages has mean 364 and standard deviation 47, and that for detective novels the number of pages has mean 404 and standard deviation 173. A reader is going to select at random one romance novel, independently select at random one detective novel, and read both books. What is the standard deviation of the total number of pages the person will read?

(A) 14.8 (B) 110.0 (C) 179.3 (D) 220.0 (E) 321.4

Answer

25. The management of a relatively new social networking website named BooglePlus is conducting a pilot study comparing use of its own site with use of a longer established social networking site named FaceList. Some articles published on the Internet give the reader the opportunity to register votes (called "likes") for the article on social networking sites to which the reader belongs. A BooglePlus employee selects from the Internet a random sample of 28 articles where the opportunity is given for registering votes for the article on both BooglePlus and FaceList. Letting x be the number of votes on FaceList and y be the number of votes on the BooglePlus, the slope of the least squares regression line of y on x is found to be 0.0623, with a standard error of 0.0224. Which of the following could be used to compute a 95% confidence interval for the slope of the population regression line of y on x?

(A) $0.0623 \pm (2.056)(0.0224)$
(B) $0.0623 \pm (2.052)(0.0224)$
(C) $0.0623 \pm (2.048)(0.0224)$
(D) $0.0224 \pm (2.056)(0.0623)$
(E) $0.0224 \pm (2.052)(0.0623)$

Answer

26. The housing units on a street have been categorized as to their type ("house" or "apartment") and occupants ("single adult," "couple only," or "with children"). The results are shown in the table below.

		Occupants			
		Single Adult	Couple Only	With Children	Total
Type of Housing Unit	House	5	14	28	47
	Apartment	25	28	20	73
	Total	30	42	48	120

Which of the following is true?

(A) There are more houses than apartments on this street.
(B) More than half of the housing units contain children.
(C) Of the three occupants categories the one with the highest proportion of apartments is "couples only."
(D) Of the two types of housing unit the one with the higher proportion categorized as "couples only" is apartments.
(E) The proportion of houses that contain couples only is smaller than the proportion of apartments that contain children.

Answer

27. A particular scale of personality was designed so that, in the country where it was formulated, the distribution of scores for the whole country was approximately normal, with mean 100 and standard deviation 15. Which of the following events is most likely?

(A) The mean personality score for a random sample of 9 people from the country is between 95 and 105
(B) The mean personality score for a random sample of 9 people from the country is between 90 and 110
(C) The mean personality score for a random sample of 16 people from the country is between 98 and 102
(D) The mean personality score for a random sample of 16 people from the country is between 95 and 105
(E) The mean personality score for a random sample of 16 people from the country is between 90 and 110

Answer

28. A computer contains on its hard drive 464 spreadsheet files. The sizes of these files, in kilobytes (KB), are summarized in the histogram below.

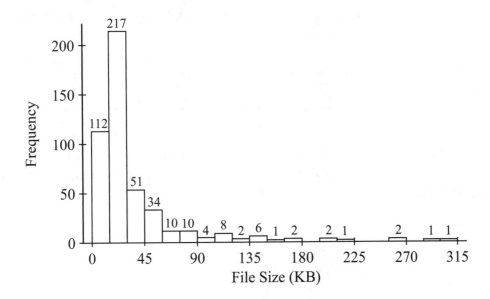

Which of the following is true about the distribution of file sizes?

(A) The median is greater than 30.
(B) The range is greater than 320.
(C) The first quartile is less than 15.
(D) The interquartile range is less than 30.
(E) The distribution is negatively skewed.

Answer

29. A company is comparing the use of two different robots for the detection of contaminants in river water. A random sample of 10 river locations is selected, and Robot 1 is used to locate a particular contaminant at those locations. Then a random sample of 15 further river locations is independently selected, and Robot 2 is used to locate the same contaminant at these locations. The sample means and standard deviations of the times taken (in minutes) to locate the contaminant are given in the table below.

	Sample Size	Mean	Standard Deviation
Robot 1	10	2.886	0.525
Robot 2	15	3.114	0.644

A two-sample t-test will be used to determine whether the results provide convincing evidence of a difference between the population mean times to locate the contaminant. Which of the following correctly calculates the test statistic?

(A) $\dfrac{2.886 - 3.114}{\sqrt{\dfrac{0.525}{10} + \dfrac{0.644}{15}}}$

(B) $\dfrac{2.886 - 3.114}{\sqrt{\dfrac{0.525}{9} + \dfrac{0.644}{14}}}$

(C) $\dfrac{2.886 - 3.114}{\sqrt{\dfrac{(0.525)^2}{10} + \dfrac{(0.644)^2}{15}}}$

(D) $\dfrac{2.886 - 3.114}{\sqrt{\dfrac{(0.525)^2}{9} + \dfrac{(0.644)^2}{14}}}$

(E) $\dfrac{2.886 - 3.114}{\sqrt{\left(\dfrac{0.525 + 0.644}{2}\right)\left(\dfrac{1}{10} + \dfrac{1}{15}\right)}}$

Answer

30. A small class consists of 8 girls and 4 boys. If a team of 4 students is selected at random, what is the probability that all the students on the team are girls?

(A) 0.141   (B) 0.198   (C) 0.255   (D) 0.312   (E) 0.369

Answer

31. A hypothesis test of the null hypothesis H_0 *versus* the alternative hypothesis H_a is performed, using a significance level of α. If the p-value for the test is greater than α, which of the following is a correct conclusion to the test?

(A) H_0 is accepted. We have convincing evidence that H_a is false.
(B) H_0 is not rejected. We do not have convincing evidence that H_a is true.
(C) H_0 is not rejected. We have convincing evidence that H_a is false.
(D) H_0 is rejected. We have convincing evidence that H_a is true.
(E) H_0 is rejected. We do not have convincing evidence that H_a is false.

Answer

Questions 32 and 33 refer to the following scenario.

A study using satellites recorded the mass of ice and the number of lightning flashes per minute in thunderstorm cells over a particular region of the country. Prior to analyzing the data, the researchers transformed both variables using logarithms (base 10). They then performed a linear regression of $\log(y)$ on $\log(x)$, where x = ice mass (in kg) and y = number of lightning flashes per minute.

32. The least squares regression line of $\log(y)$ on $\log(x)$ resulting from the regression analysis was

    $$\text{predicted value of } \log(y) = -0.285 + 0.2255 \log(x).$$

    What does the model predict for the number of lightning flashes per minute when the ice mass is 66,000,000 kg?

    (A) 2.1   (B) 5.9   (C) 16.8   (D) 23.8   (E) 30.1

    Answer

33. The regression analysis produced the following residual plot.

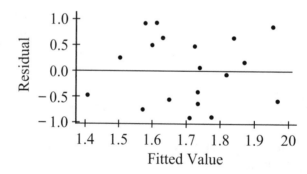

    According to the residual plot, does a linear regression appear to be appropriate for modeling the relationship between the transformed variables?

    (A) Yes, because the residual plot shows a random pattern.
    (B) Yes, because the vertical spread of points in the residual plot is roughly centered about the horizontal axis that represents a zero residual.
    (C) No, because there is no sign of a clear curve in the residual plot.
    (D) No, because the best fit line in the residual plot is roughly horizontal.
    (E) No, because logarithms base 10 were used, when natural logarithms are more appropriate for use with physical data.

    Answer

34. When two cubes, each with faces numbered 1 through 6, are rolled, what is the probability that the total score is 11?

(A) $\frac{1}{36}$ (B) $\frac{1}{24}$ (C) $\frac{1}{18}$ (D) $\frac{1}{12}$ (E) $\frac{1}{6}$

Answer

35. There are large numbers of jobs available in Town A and in Town B. A researcher selects a sample of 97 jobs available in Town A and a sample of 94 jobs available in Town B. The salaries offered for the jobs in the samples are noted, and the results will used to construct a confidence interval for $\mu_A - \mu_B$, where μ_A is the mean salary for all jobs available in Town A and μ_B is the mean salary for all jobs available in Town B. Which of the following is NOT true about construction of the confidence interval, and the interval that is obtained?

(A) It is necessary to assume that the samples are independent and random.
(B) It is necessary to assume that the population distributions are normal.
(C) A t-distribution could be used.
(D) The quantity $\overline{x}_A - \overline{x}_B$ will lie at the center of the interval, where $\overline{x}_A$ and $\overline{x}_B$ are the sample means for Town A and Town B, respectively.
(E) If larger samples had been used, then the confidence interval would probably have been narrower.

Answer

36. A student at a kindergarten-through-12th-grade private school takes a sample of students at the school, and finds, amongst the students in the sample, a positive association between the sizes of their feet and how fast they can run. The student concludes, "All other things being equal, if you want a faster runner you should probably choose someone with large feet." A teacher responds, "That doesn't follow! Kids with bigger feet tend to be older, and older kids tend to be faster runners. For students of the same age, running speed might have nothing to do with foot size!" Which of the following is being considered a confounding variable in this context?

(A) Method of sampling
(B) Method of measuring running speed
(C) Foot size
(D) Age
(E) Running speed

Answer

37. The masses of the berries produced by a particular type of tree can be assumed to be normally distributed with a standard deviation of 72 milligrams. If a berry of this type is selected at random, which of the following represents the probability that the mass of the berry is within 54 milligrams of the mean mass of berries of this type?

(A) $P(z < 0.75)$
(B) $P(z < -0.75)$
(C) $P(z > 0.75)$
(D) $P(z < -0.75) + P(z > 0.75)$
(E) $P(z < 0.75) - P(z < -0.75)$

Answer

38. A simple random sample is selected from a population, and a measurement is taken for each individual in the sample. Using these results, the 95% confidence interval for the population mean is found to be (58.770, 61.428). (The conditions for construction of the interval were checked and verified.) The results from the same sample are now to be used to perform a hypothesis test. If a significance level of $\alpha = 0.05$ is used, which of the following is true?

(A) In a test of $H_0: \mu = 57$ against $H_a: \mu \neq 57$, H_0 would be rejected.
(B) In a test of $H_0: \mu = 57$ against $H_a: \mu < 57$, H_0 would be rejected.
(C) In a test of $H_0: \mu = 59$ against $H_a: \mu \neq 59$, H_0 would be rejected.
(D) In a test of $H_0: \mu = 60$ against $H_a: \mu > 60$, H_0 would be rejected.
(E) In a test of $H_0: \mu = 62$ against $H_a: \mu < 62$, H_0 would not be rejected.

Answer

39. Forty volunteers have been gathered as subjects in an experiment to compare two treatments. These experimental subjects will be randomly assigned to two groups, each of size 20. Random assignment to the groups ensures that

(A) the groups are exactly the same with respect to any variable that might have an effect on a person's response to either of the treatments
(B) any initial differences between the people in the two groups occur completely by chance
(C) the results of the experiment will be the same for the two groups
(D) the participants won't know which treatment they are receiving
(E) the people will not be in the same group as their friends

Answer

40. In which of the following scenarios could a two-proportion z-test be used for the hypothesis test mentioned? (In the scenario or scenarios where the two-proportion z-test is appropriate, you may assume that the conditions for use of the test are met.)

I. A random sample of adults is selected from Neighborhood A and an independent random sample of adults is selected from Neighborhood B. Each adult selected is asked this question: "If you're shopping in a supermarket and the total bill is between $10 and $20, do you prefer to pay using cash or some other method?" A hypothesis test is used to compare the proportions of adults in the two neighborhoods responding that they would use cash.

II. A random sample of adults is selected from Neighborhood A and an independent random sample of adults is selected from Neighborhood B. Each adult selected is asked this question: "If you're shopping in a supermarket and the total bill is between $10 and $20, do you prefer to pay using cash, a debit card, or a credit card?" A hypothesis test is used to compare the proportions of adults falling into the three categories for the two neighborhoods.

III. The cashiers at a supermarket are given instructions as to how to randomly assign each customer (without the customer knowing) to either Group A or Group B. Customers assigned to Group A will be asked "Would you like to use cash or a card for your payment?" Customers assigned to Group B will be asked "Would you like to use a card or cash for your payment?" A hypothesis test is used to compare the proportions of customers in the two groups who choose to use cash.

(A) I only
(B) II only
(C) I and II
(D) I and III
(E) II and III

Answer

SECTION II
Part A
Questions 1–5
Spend about 65 minutes on this part of the exam.
Percent of Section II grade—75

Directions: Show all your work. Indicate clearly the methods you use, because you will be graded on the correctness of your method as well as on the accuracy and completeness of your results and explanations.

1. An experiment was conducted to compare the influence of an adult of the same sex with that of an adult of the opposite sex in terms of nurturing behavior in children. The experiment used 72 nursery school children aged 3 to 6, and the children were randomly assigned to three groups, with 24 children in each group.

   In the first group, named the "Same-sex adult" group, each child was placed in a room along with some appealing activities such as colored pens and blank coloring books. At the same time, an adult of the same sex as the child was seated in another part of the room with various items including some furry toys. For 10 minutes, the adult showed strong nurturing behavior toward the furry toys while the child played in the other part of the room. Then, for 20 minutes, the child was given unsupervised access to same items as those the adult had used, including the furry toys. During this time the child was observed, and the number of nurturing acts shown towards the furry toys by the child was noted.

   The children in the second group, the "Different-sex adult" group, were given the same treatment as those in the first group, except that the adult model was of the opposite sex to that of the child. Each child's behavior was measured in the same way as in first group.

   Children in the third group, the control group, were given the same treatment, except that the adult involved did not show nurturing behavior towards the toys. (In this group, the sex of the adult was chosen randomly.) Each child's behavior was measured in the same way as in the first two groups.

The results of the experiment are summarized in the boxplots below.

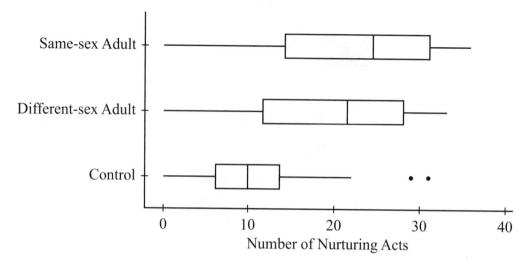

(a) Compare the distributions of the number of nurturing acts among the three groups.

(b) For the "Same-sex adult" group, would the mean most likely have been greater than the median, or less than the median? Explain how you reach your conclusion.

2. A consumer organization compared the screen sizes and prices of fourteen global positioning system (GPS) units. The fourteen GPS units used in the study included units with screen sizes as small as 3.5 inches and as large as 7 inches. Prices ranged between $90 and $230. Some computer output from a regression analysis of these data is shown below.

Predictor	Coef	StDev	T	P
Constant	-9.47	29.65	-0.32	0.755
Screen size	32.461	6.777	4.79	0.000

S = 22.3293   R-Sq = 65.7%   R-Sq(adj) = 62.8%

(a) Using the computer output, write the equation of the least squares regression line that describes the relationship between price and screen size.

(b) Suppose that two GPS units are selected, and the screen sizes of the two units differ by 4 inches. According to the least squares regression line, how much more than the unit with the smaller screen is the one with the larger screen expected to cost?

(c) What does the least squares regression line predict for the price of a GPS unit whose screen size is 6.5 inches?

A scatterplot for this data set, including the least squares regression line, is shown below.

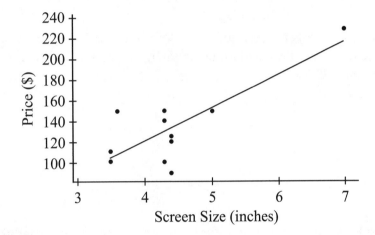

(d) Suppose that the GPS unit with a screen size of 7 inches were to be removed from the data set. Would the line shown in the scatterplot provide the best description of the relationship for the remaining data values? Why, or why not?

3. A study conducted at a large hospital found that 27.8 percent of all patients admitted to the hospital's intensive care unit (ICU) remained in the ICU for less than 24 hours.

   (a) If 8 patients are selected at random from the ICU patients at this hospital, what is the probability that 2 or fewer of them remained in the ICU for less than 24 hours?

   (b) Suppose that 20 patients are selected at random from the ICU patients at this hospital. Calculate the mean and the standard deviation of the number of these patients who remained in the ICU for less than 24 hours.

   (c) Another result of the study was that for elective (non-emergency) admissions to the hospital's ICU, the length of stay in the ICU had a mean of 18.9 hours and a standard deviation of 3.9 hours. Assuming that the length of stay in the ICU for elective admissions is approximately normally distributed, what proportion of elective admissions remained in the ICU for less than 24 hours?

4. The current inventory of a library consists of 198,233 items. The items are categorized as journals, books, DVDs, and other media. The numbers of items falling into the four categories are given in the table below.

Category	Journals	Books	DVDs	Other
Number of Items	124327	56340	10469	7097

(a) Complete the table below showing the proportions of the entire inventory falling into the given categories.

Category	Journals	Books	DVDs	Other
Proportion of Inventory		0.284		

(b) The chief librarian is preparing a report regarding the patterns of use of the library. To assist with this, a coworker compiles data regarding library use during the previous week. The numbers of items used in the four categories during that week are shown in the table below.

Category	Journals	Books	DVDs	Other
Number of Items Used	600	353	58	30

The librarians are willing to treat the uses of the library during that week as a random sample from the set of all uses of the library. Do these results provide convincing evidence that the proportions of all uses that fall into the four categories are different from the proportions of items in those categories (the numbers in the table in part (a))? Provide statistical evidence to support your answer.

5. A student who is writing an article about music for the school newspaper asks another student, Chin-Sun, to estimate the mean length of the mp3 downloads available on a particular web site. Being an AP Statistics student, Chin-Sun decides to make this estimate using a confidence interval. She randomly selects 15 songs from the site, and makes note of their lengths in seconds. Chin-Sun then uses these results to construct a 95% confidence interval for the mean length of all songs on the site. Prior to gathering this sample, Chin-Sun has no knowledge of the lengths of the songs on the site.

    (a) In order to find the critical value to use in the calculation of her confidence interval, should Chin-Sun use the standard normal (z) distribution or a t distribution? Explain your answer.

    (b) What is the meaning of 95% confidence in this context?

    (c) Using the results from her sample, Chin-Sun checks and verifies all the conditions for inference, and correctly calculates the confidence interval for the mean length (in seconds) of all songs on the site to be 242.733 ± 19.209. What was the standard deviation of the song lengths in Chin-Sun's sample?

SECTION II
Part B
Question 6
Spend about 25 minutes on this part of the exam.
Percent of Section II grade—25

Directions: Show all your work. Indicate clearly the methods you use, because you will be graded on the correctness of your method as well as on the accuracy and completeness of your results and explanations.

6. The owner of a small company is planning an economic impact study that will include information about local spending by the company's employees. Spending information is gathered by means of a detailed survey, and so the owner initially plans to select a simple random sample of 8 employees, and require only those 8 people to complete the survey. The company has 32 employees in total.

   (a) Explain how the simple random sample of 8 employees might be selected.

The company's 32 employees are paid at three grade levels: 16 at the "Individual Contributor" level, 12 at the "Professional" level, and 4 at the "Managerial" level. A statistician advising the owner suggests use of a stratified random sample consisting of 4 individual contributors, 3 professionals, and 1 manager.

(b) Why would it be sensible, for the purposes of this study, to stratify by employee grade level?

The economic impact study will include an estimate of the mean local spending for the 32 employees of the company. The statistician wishes to explain further the benefit of using the stratified sampling method described above for estimation of this mean. In order to do this, the statistician creates a list of hypothetical annual local spending values for all 32 employees. These values (in thousands of dollars, rounded to the nearest one-thousand), along with the employees' grade levels, are shown in the table on the next page. (The employees have been sorted according to their hypothetical annual spending values.)

Employee Number	Grade Level	Hypothetical Annual Spending (in thousands of dollars)
5	Individual	9
1	Individual	10
3	Individual	11
2	Individual	13
4	Individual	13
11	Individual	13
14	Individual	13
9	Individual	14
16	Individual	14
6	Individual	15
10	Individual	15
13	Individual	15
23	Professional	15
24	Professional	15
7	Individual	17
8	Individual	17
12	Individual	17
28	Professional	17
15	Individual	18
18	Professional	18
19	Professional	18
20	Professional	18
17	Professional	19
25	Professional	19
26	Professional	19
27	Professional	19
21	Professional	20
22	Professional	20
30	Managerial	20
29	Managerial	22
32	Managerial	22
31	Managerial	26

Suppose that a simple random sample of 8 employees is used for the study, and that the hypothetical spending values given in the table are true. Then the smallest possible sample mean for the 8 employees selected is given by

$$\overline{x}_{min} = \frac{9 + 10 + 11 + 13 + 13 + 13 + 13 + 14}{8} = 12,$$

and the largest possible sample mean is given by

$$\overline{x}_{max} = \frac{19 + 19 + 20 + 20 + 20 + 22 + 22 + 26}{8} = 21.$$

(c) Suppose, now, that the stratified sampling method described before part (b) is used. Assuming that the spending values given in the table are true, find the smallest and largest possible values of the sample mean, and add your values to the number line given. (The number line also shows the mean hypothetical spending for all employees, which is 17.5.)

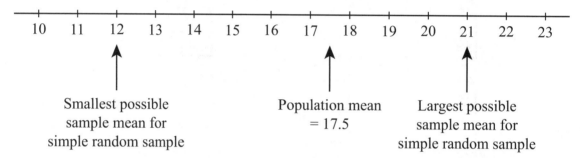

(d) The answer to part (c) suggests that one of the two sampling methods produces a sample mean that has a smaller variability than the sample mean produced by the other sampling method. Which of the two sampling methods is this? Explain how you reach your conclusion.

(e) It is known that, over all possible samples, the two sampling methods will both produce sample means that are, on average, equal to the population mean of 17.5. Use your answer to part (d) to explain why, for estimation of the population mean, the stratified random sampling described here would be preferable to simple random sampling.

Sample Examination Three

SECTION I
Time—1 hour and 30 minutes
Number of questions—40
Percent of total grade—50

Directions: Solve each of the following problems, using the available space for scratch work. Decide which is the best of the choices given and fill in the corresponding oval on the answer sheet. No credit will be given for anything written in the test book. Do not spend too much time on any one problem.

1. A company has recently given some pay raises. The distribution of the amounts by which the employees' salaries have been increased is illustrated by the boxplot below.

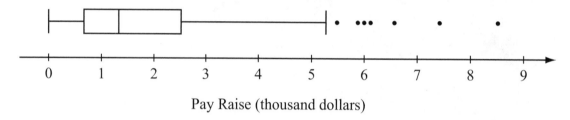

Pay Raise (thousand dollars)

Which of the following best describes the shape of the distribution and the interquartile range (IQR) of the salary increases?

(A) symmetrical; IQR is approximately $700
(B) skewed to the right; IQR is approximately $700
(C) skewed to the left; IQR is approximately $700
(D) skewed to the right; IQR is approximately $2000
(E) skewed to the left; IQR is approximately $2000

Answer

146

2. A researcher is studying an old edition of an encyclopedia. She wishes to estimate the proportion of the printed matter in the encyclopedia that is diagrams and pictures (as opposed to text). The encyclopedia consists of 30 volumes, and she observes that the proportion of printed matter that is diagrams and pictures is roughly the same in each of the volumes. The researcher randomly selects four of the volumes, and then studies every page in those four volumes. This is an example of which type of sampling?

(A) Cluster
(B) Convenience
(C) Simple random
(D) Stratified random
(E) Systematic

Answer

3. A company produces cloth for use in airplane seats. The company claims that the mean breaking strength μ for specimens of the cloth is 80 pounds of force, but the airlines who buy the cloth are concerned that the cloth might be weaker than that. A group working on behalf of the airlines takes a random sample of specimens of the cloth and finds the breaking strength of each specimen in the sample. What hypotheses should the group use to test the manufacturer's claim?

(A) $H_0: \mu = 80$, $H_a: \mu < 80$
(B) $H_0: \mu = 80$, $H_a: \mu \neq 80$
(C) $H_0: \mu = 80$, $H_a: \mu > 80$
(D) $H_0: \mu < 80$, $H_a: \mu = 80$
(E) $H_0: \mu > 80$, $H_a: \mu = 80$

Answer

4. In a company, 78% of the employees opt for medical insurance and 42% of the employees opt for life insurance. 82% of the employees opt for at least one of these benefits. What percent of the employees opt for both of these benefits?

(A) 4%   (B) 18%   (C) 33%   (D) 38%   (E) 40%

Answer

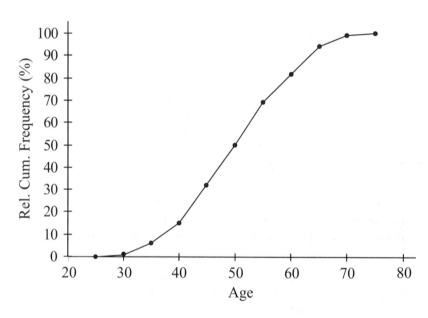

5. A society has 160 members. A relative cumulative frequency graph of their ages is shown in the figure above. Approximately how many of the society's members are over 43 years old?

(A) 25   (B) 40   (C) 48   (D) 75   (E) 120

Answer

6. A track and field coach wants to find out whether a particular hammer thrower performs better, on average, in the morning or in the afternoon. The coach observes a random sample of the athlete's morning throws and a random sample of the athlete's afternoon throws. Which one of the following significance tests could be used to analyze the results?

(A) One-sample t-test for a mean
(B) Two-sample t-test for means
(C) Paired t-test
(D) One-proportion z-test
(E) Two-proportion z-test

Answer

7. Diana has several children and each of her children has several friends, so she can never be sure how many children will come to dinner. However, over long experience she has worked out that the probability distribution for the number of children who will come to dinner is as shown below.

Number of children	0	1	2	3	4	5	6	7	8	9	10
Probability	0.01	0.04	0.13	0.15	0.16	0.17	0.12	0.09	0.07	0.04	0.02

On any given evening, what is the minimum number of places that she should set at the dinner table for the children in order to be at least 80% sure that all the children can be seated?

(A) 6   (B) 7   (C) 8   (D) 9   (E) 10

Answer

8. A machine produces metal springs for computer lids. Over a long period of time it has been found that 10% of the springs produced by the machine are defective. After some adjustments to the machine, a random sample of 200 springs is selected and it is found that 16 of the springs in the sample are defective. The appropriate significance test is carried out in order to determine whether the proportion of defective springs has changed. Which of the following is the correct p-value for the test?

(A) $2 \cdot P\left(z < \dfrac{0.08 - 0.1}{\sqrt{\dfrac{(0.1)(0.9)}{200}}}\right)$

(B) $2 \cdot P\left(z > \dfrac{0.08 - 0.1}{\sqrt{\dfrac{(0.1)(0.9)}{200}}}\right)$

(C) $2 \cdot P\left(z < \dfrac{0.08 - 0.1}{\sqrt{\dfrac{(.08)(.92)}{200}}}\right)$

(D) $2 \cdot P\left(z > \dfrac{0.08 - 0.1}{\sqrt{\dfrac{(.08)(.92)}{200}}}\right)$

(E) $\dfrac{1}{2} \cdot P\left(z < \dfrac{0.08 - 0.1}{\sqrt{\dfrac{(.08)(.92)}{200}}}\right)$

Answer

[ ]

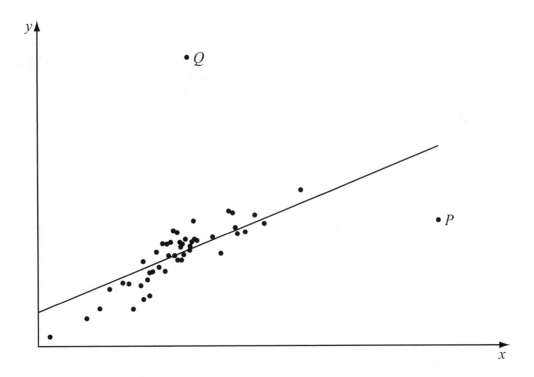

9. The scatterplot above shows 52 points with the associated least squares regression line for predicting values of y from values of x. One of the two labeled points – either P or Q – will be removed. Which of the following is true?

(A) Removal of the point P would substantially increase the slope of the least squares regression line. Removal of the point Q would have little effect on the slope of the least squares regression line.

(B) Removal of the point P would substantially decrease the slope of the least squares regression line. Removal of the point Q would have little effect on the slope of the least squares regression line.

(C) Removal of the point Q would substantially increase the slope of the least squares regression line. Removal of the point P would have little effect on the slope of the least squares regression line.

(D) Removal of the point Q would substantially decrease the slope of the least squares regression line. Removal of the point P would have little effect on the slope of the least squares regression line.

(E) Removal of the point P would have a substantial effect on the slope of the least squares regression line <u>and</u> removal of the point Q would have a substantial effect on the slope of the least squares regression line.

Answer

10. In a particular country it is known that 40% of the residents have blue eyes, 35% of the residents have brown eyes, and 25% of the residents have green eyes. A student carries out a study to determine whether, in terms of color, the eyes of dolls manufactured in that country are representative of the residents of the country. The student takes a random sample of 40 brands of doll, and finds that 10 of them have blue eyes, 19 of them have brown eyes, and 11 of them have green eyes. She then carries out the appropriate significance test and obtains the p-value for the test. Which of the following is true?

(A) The p-value is between 0 and 0.05.
(B) The p-value is between 0.05 and 0.1.
(C) The p-value is between 0.1 and 0.15.
(D) The p-value is between 0.15 and 0.2.
(E) The p-value is greater than 0.2.

Answer

11. When Joe plays a board game with his four sisters, any one of the five players is equally likely to win. They decide to play the game repeatedly until Joe wins a game, and then they will stop. Assuming that the outcomes of the games are independent, what is the probability that they play at least three games?

(A) 0.128   (B) 0.312   (C) 0.488   (D) 0.512   (E) 0.640

Answer

12. A vending machine delivers varying amounts of coffee. The standard deviation of the amount per serving is known, but the mean amount per serving has recently been adjusted to an unknown value. The person responsible for the machine takes ten servings of coffee from the machine, and is willing to assume that these ten servings form a random sample. She calculates the sample mean serving size to be 10.8 ounces.

She now intends to carry out a z-test about the mean serving size μ for all servings of coffee from this machine. Which of the following pairs of hypotheses will result in the smallest p-value?

(A) $H_0: \mu = 10$, $H_a: \mu < 10$
(B) $H_0: \mu = 10$, $H_a: \mu > 10$
(C) $H_0: \mu = 11$, $H_a: \mu < 11$
(D) $H_0: \mu = 11$, $H_a: \mu \neq 11$
(E) $H_0: \mu = 11$, $H_a: \mu > 11$

Answer

13. A student named Russell does a survey concerning the amount of sleep his fellow students are getting. Having taken a sample of students and asked each student the total amount of sleep he/she has had over the past week, he discovers that one of the responses is an outlier. Russell strongly suspects that this response was untrue, but he does not feel able to exclude it from his data set. In order to summarize the center and the spread of the complete set of responses he should quote the

(A) mean and the standard deviation
(B) mean and the interquartile range
(C) mean and the range
(D) median and the interquartile range
(E) median and the range

Answer

14. In a high school there are 638 underclassmen (9th and 10th graders) and 523 upperclassmen (11th and 12th graders). Of the underclassmen 83.1% take the bus to school, and of the upperclassmen 70.9% take the bus to school. If a student is chosen at random from those students who take the bus to school, what is the probability that this student is an underclassman?

(A) 0.457   (B) 0.550   (C) 0.588   (D) 0.671   (E) 0.831

Answer

15. A survey is conducted to compare the proportions of men and women who access their bank statements online. Denoting the population proportions by p_M and p_W, a two-proportion z-test is carried out to test $H_0 : p_M = p_W$ against $H_a : p_M > p_W$. The value of the test statistic is found to be $z = 0.784$, and the p-value for the test is found to be 0.216. Which of the following is a correct interpretation of the p-value?

(A) Given the results of the survey, the probability that $p_M > p_W$ is 0.216.
(B) Given the results of the survey, the probability that $p_M = p_W$ is 0.216.
(C) Given that $p_M = p_W$, the probability of getting a value of z at least as large as 0.784 is 0.216.
(D) Given that $p_M > p_W$, the probability of getting a value of z at least as large as 0.784 is 0.216.
(E) Given that $p_M \neq p_W$, the probability of getting a value of z at least as large as 0.784 is 0.216.

Answer

16. A school district currently allows 12th graders at the high school to drive to school. The Board of Education is considering withdrawing this policy, and wishes to determine the opinions of the parents of students in grades K–12 on the issue.

The Board has a list of email addresses covering the parents of most of the students in the district. An email containing the following message is sent to the parents on the list.

```
Please read the following statement:

"12th graders should not be allowed to drive to
school. The reduction in parking would allow for a
substantial expansion in student activities."

Do you strongly agree, agree, disagree, strongly
disagree, or have no opinion? Please reply with
your response.
```

After three days, the responses are gathered and are analyzed. Which of the following could NOT be considered a source of bias in this study?

(A) The statement is worded in a way that is likely to influence the reader in a particular direction.
(B) The message is sent to parents of students who are not in the 12th grade.
(C) The list of email addresses does not include the parents of all students in the district.
(D) Some parents will not read the email within the three-day period.
(E) Some parents who read the email will choose not to respond.

Answer

17. For a group of students, the correlation between their heights (in inches) and their weights (in pounds) is 0.332. You are given that 1 inch = 2.54 centimeters and that 1 pound = 0.454 kilogram. If the heights are expressed in centimeters and the weights are expressed in kilograms, what will be the value of the correlation?

A) 0.059   (B) 0.288   (C) 0.332   (D) 0.383   (E) 1.857

Answer

18. A track and field coach has observed two javelin throwers for a long period of time, and now has to select one of them for the team. Which of the following would NOT be a good reason to choose thrower A in preference to B?

(A) The mean for thrower A is greater than the mean for thrower B.
(B) The median for thrower A is greater than the median for thrower B.
(C) The third quartile for thrower A is greater than the third quartile for thrower B.
(D) The maximum for thrower A is greater than the maximum for thrower B.
(E) The distribution of A's throws is positively skewed whereas the distribution of B's throws is roughly symmetrical.

Answer

19. A company is developing a new drug for reducing the symptoms of pollen allergies. They have developed two forms of the drug: A and B. The company wants to find out which form of the drug is most effective and to determine whether the amount to be taken each day should be split into one, two, or three doses. A set of volunteers who suffer from pollen allergies is split into six groups to receive treatments according to the following table.

	1 Dose	2 Doses	3 Doses
Drug A			
Drug B			

How many explanatory variables (factors) are there in this experiment?

(A) 1   (B) 2   (C) 3   (D) 5   (E) 6

Answer

20. An airline observes a random sample of its flights on a particular route. The 95% confidence interval for the mean time (in minutes) for all flights on this route is calculated to be (47.0, 53.0). Which of the following is NOT true?

   (A) At the 95% confidence level, the true mean flight time is within 3.0 minutes of the sample mean flight time.

   (B) If the true mean flight time were outside the interval (47.0, 53.0) then the sample mean that was found would be very unlikely.

   (C) Approximately $2\frac{1}{2}$% of flights on this route are longer than 53 minutes.

   (D) We are 95% confident that the true mean flight time is between 47.0 and 53.0 minutes.

   (E) If many random samples of the same size were taken and the 95% confidence intervals were calculated, then 95% of the confidence intervals would contain the true mean flight time.

Answer

21. A "population" is formed by placing five balls in a bag. The balls are labeled 1, 2, 3, 4, and 5, respectively. The mean of this population is $\mu = 3$. Someone who does not know the contents of the bag will estimate the value of μ by randomly taking a sample of three of the balls (without replacement) and finding <u>either</u> the sample mean <u>or</u> the sample median.

In the meantime, a statistician has listed all the possible samples of size three (sampling without replacement) and has calculated the sample mean and the sample median for each possible sample. The statistician finds that:

- All the possible sample <u>means</u> form a distribution whose mean is 3 and whose standard deviation is 0.577.
- All the possible sample <u>medians</u> form a distribution whose mean is 3 and whose standard deviation is 0.775.

Regarding the choice between using the sample mean and using the sample median for estimating μ, which of the following is true?

(A) Both the sample mean and the sample median are unbiased, but the sample median is preferable as it has the larger standard deviation.
(B) Both the sample mean and the sample median are unbiased, but the sample mean is preferable as it has the smaller standard deviation.
(C) The sample mean is unbiased and the sample median is biased, so the sample mean is preferable.
(D) The sample median is unbiased and the sample mean is biased, so the sample median is preferable.
(E) Both the sample mean and the sample median are biased.

Answer

22. A set of cards cards consists of 12 red cards (numbered 1–12), 12 purple cards (numbered 1–12), 12 green cards (numbered 1–12), and 12 yellow cards (numbered 1–12). One card is going to be picked at random. Let *A* be the event that the card is green and let *B* be the event that the card is a 12. Which of the following is true?

(A) The events *A* and *B* are independent and mutually exclusive.
(B) The events *A* and *B* are independent but not mutually exclusive.
(C) The events *A* and *B* are not independent but are mutually exclusive.
(D) The events *A* and *B* are not independent and not mutually exclusive.
(E) It is not possible to tell from the information given whether or not the events *A* and *B* are mutually exclusive.

Answer

23. A new warm-up procedure has been suggested for use before working out, and it is hoped that the procedure will encourage a greater increase in muscle mass. In order to test this, a study is designed using 40 volunteers who already work out regularly.

The volunteers will be randomly split into two groups, each of size 20. The first group will be taught the warm-up exercises and will be supervised doing the exercises prior to their regular workouts. The second group will merely continue with their regular workouts. At the beginning and at the end of the study, the muscle mass of each of the volunteers will be measured by people who do not know which volunteers were in which group.

Which of the following is NOT the case in the study described?

(A) This study is an experiment.
(B) Randomization is used.
(C) A control group is used.
(D) The study is conducted in a double-blind manner.
(E) There is no blocking involved in the study.

Answer

24. A set of scores has mean 70.3 and a standard deviation 8.8. The scores are now scaled according to the formula $y = 0.7x + 30$, where x is the old score and y is the new score. What is the standard deviation of the new scores?

    (A) 4.31   (B) 6.16   (C) 7.36   (D) 36.16   (E) 37.36

    Answer

25. In a high school, all of the 11th graders take both math and physics. After the students have taken the midyear exam in both subjects, the physics teachers are considering the results, and have found the value of r^2, the square of the correlation coefficient between the math scores and the physics scores. Which of the following is best answered by consideration of the value of r^2 ?

    (A) Whether high physics scores are associated with high math scores
    (B) Whether the relationship between physics scores and math scores would be better represented by a curve or a straight line
    (C) To what extent the variation in physics scores can be explained by a linear relationship between physics scores and math scores
    (D) Whether there is an outlier in the scatterplot of physics scores and math scores
    (E) Whether the physics scores are on the whole higher than the math scores

    Answer

26. In a random sample of 400 adults, each person stated his or her political preference. The sex (male/female) of each respondent was also noted. The results are shown in the table below.

	Democrat	Republican	Other
Male	94	78	18
Female	88	86	36

If political preference is independent of sex, which of the following is the expected number of respondents who are female and support the Democratic Party?

(A) 40.04   (B) 46.20   (C) 86.45   (D) 95.55   (E) 103.895

Answer

27. Suppose that an observational study has shown that people who regularly consume substantial amounts of olive oil live longer lives, on average, than those who do not. Of the following arguments, which is strongest in explaining why the result of the study does <u>not</u> imply that in order to live longer one should start to regularly consume substantial amounts of olive oil?

(A) Olive oil is high in fat, and it's not a good idea to eat high-fat foods.
(B) There are many other factors contributing to how long you live that were not considered by the study.
(C) If a person is recorded as eating substantial amounts of olive oil and living a long life, we don't know whether the long life was caused by the olive oil eating or, for example, regular exercise.
(D) People who choose to include substantial amounts of olive oil in their diets might well be the sort of people who have healthier lifestyles in general, and a healthy lifestyle leads to a long life.
(E) Olive oil is associated with frying, and frying is unhealthy.

Answer

28. A team of psychologists is studying the behavior of the students in a first grade class. There are 16 girls and 16 boys in the class, and for each student the psychologists record the number of minutes "on task" during a forty minute class. The team wishes to compare the on-task times of the girls with the on-task times of the boys. Which of the following would NOT be a suitable graph for displaying the results?

(A) Parallel dotplots with equal scales
(B) Back-to-back stemplot
(C) Histograms with equal scales
(D) Side-by-side boxplots
(E) Scatterplot with girls' times plotted as x-values and boys' times plotted as y-values

Answer

29. The amount of flour per bag delivered by a machine is known to have a standard deviation of 0.4 ounce. What is the minimum sample size required to estimate the mean amount of flour per bag to within 0.1 ounce with 95% confidence?

(A) 3   (B) 8   (C) 43   (D) 62   (E) 154

Answer

30. In the context of z- and t-tests for the mean using small samples, which of the following is (are) true?

    I.   The z-test requires the assumption that the population distribution is normal.
    II. The t-test requires the assumption that the population distribution is normal.
    III. The t-test is used when the population standard deviation is unknown.

(A) I only
(B) I and II only
(C) I and III only
(D) II and III only
(E) I, II, and III

Answer

31. When a large number of a particular type of seed is planted, it is known that 70% of the seeds will germinate. In addition, the germination of any one seed is independent of the germination of any other seed. If 20 of the seeds are planted, what are the mean and the standard deviation of the number of seeds that germinate?

(A) mean = 0.7, standard deviation = 0.102
(B) mean = 0.7, standard deviation = 0.458
(C) mean = 14, standard deviation = 0.102
(D) mean = 14, standard deviation = 2.049
(E) mean = 14, standard deviation = 4.2

Answer

32. A company has a machine that produces cans of coconut milk, and it has been noticed that the amount of coconut milk varies from can to can. The amounts are normally distributed with standard deviation 8 milliliters. The label used on the cans states that each can contains 414 milliliters. The management of the company decides to set the mean μ of the amount of coconut milk per can so that 98% of the cans contain more than 414 milliliters. Of the following, which is the closest to the amount (in milliliters) to which μ should be set?

    (A) 395.4   (B) 397.6   (C) 421.8   (D) 430.4   (E) 432.6

Answer

33. A political party wishes to estimate the proportion of voters that support the party in a particular state. The party will poll a random sample of n voters from the state. Which of the following is likely to result in the smallest margin of error?

    (A) $n = 400$, confidence level = 95%
    (B) $n = 400$, confidence level = 98%
    (C) $n = 400$, confidence level = 99%
    (D) $n = 500$, confidence level = 95%
    (E) $n = 500$, confidence level = 99%

Answer

34. A pharmaceutical company wishes to compare the effectiveness of three drugs, A, B, and C, that are designed to reduce blood pressure. The company believes that the younger a person is, the more likely he is to respond to a drug of this sort. The company intends to design an experiment in which each subject will be instructed to take one of the drugs regularly for a four week period. Each subject's blood pressure will be measured at the beginning and at the end of the four week period.

There are three young men, three middle-aged men, and three elderly men available to take part in this study. Which of the following is the most appropriate method for assigning the treatment groups?

(A) For each man, randomly choose which drug he will be given.

(B) From the whole set of nine men, randomly choose three to receive drug A, three to receive B, and three to receive C.

(C) For the three young men, randomly assign one man to drug A, one man to drug B, and one man to drug C; repeat this process for the middle-aged men and for the elderly men.

(D) Randomly choose one of the drugs, and give that drug to all the young men; randomly choose one of the remaining drugs and give that to all the middle-aged men; and then give the third drug to all the elderly men.

(E) Randomly pick one man from each age group and from these three randomly assign one to drug A, one to drug B, and one to drug C; then pick another man from each age group and do the same thing; then do the same thing for the remaining three men.

Answer

35. A manufacturer of tires has used a particular type of rubber for a long time, and has established over the years that the mean life of the tires is 40,000 miles. However, the company has now changed the type of rubber used and needs to find out whether the mean life of the tires has changed. Having tested a random sample of the tires, a t-test for the mean is carried out using H_0: $\mu = 40{,}000$ *versus* H_a: $\mu \neq 40{,}000$. The t-value for the test is found to be -1.902 and the p-value is found to be 0.063. Using a 5% significance level, which of the following is a correct conclusion for the test?

(A) Since $p > 0.05$ we do not have sufficient evidence to conclude that the mean life of the tires is not equal to 40,000 miles.

(B) Since $p > 0.05$ we do not have sufficient evidence to conclude that the mean life of the tires is less than 40,000 miles.

(C) Since $p > 0.05$ we have sufficient evidence to conclude that the mean life of the tires is equal to 40,000 miles.

(D) Since $p > 0.05$ we have sufficient evidence to conclude that the mean life of the tires is not equal to 40,000 miles.

(E) Since $p > 0.05$ we have sufficient evidence to conclude that the mean life of the tires is greater than 40,000 miles.

Answer

36. A very large population has standard deviation denoted by σ. A random sample of size n will be taken from this population. The quantity $\dfrac{\sigma}{\sqrt{n}}$ is

(A) the mean of the distribution of the sample standard deviation

(B) the standard deviation of the sampling distribution of the sample mean

(C) the standard deviation of the sample

(D) an estimate of the population standard deviation

(E) an estimate of the sample standard deviation calculated from the population standard deviation

Answer

37. In a test of the null hypothesis H_0: $\mu = 50$ against the alternative hypothesis H_a: $\mu < 50$, with significance level α using sample size n, which of the following is the smallest?

    (A) The probability of Type II error when $\mu = 48$, given that $n = 40$ and $\alpha = 0.05$
    (B) The probability of Type II error when $\mu = 46$, given that $n = 40$ and $\alpha = 0.05$
    (C) The probability of Type II error when $\mu = 48$, given that $n = 40$ and $\alpha = 0.01$
    (D) The probability of Type II error when $\mu = 46$, given that $n = 40$ and $\alpha = 0.01$
    (E) The probability of Type II error when $\mu = 48$, given that $n = 20$ and $\alpha = 0.05$

Answer

38. Having graded a test, a teacher was interested in the relationship between the amount of time the students studied for the test and the scores they received. She asked the 24 students individually how much they studied, and then compiled a list giving for each student the amount of time studied and the score on the test. The teacher performed a least squares regression analysis. Part of the computer output from that analysis is shown below.

```
Dependent variable: Score on test

Predictor        Coef      SE Coef          T            P
Constant    69.555194    3.721432       18.69      <.0001
Time         0.2642443    0.109216        2.42      0.0243

S = 6.3241     R-sq = 21.0%    R-sq (adj) = 17.5%
```

Which of the following is a 99% confidence interval for the slope of the regression line that relates the time spent studying and the score on the test?

    (A) $69.555 \pm (2.807)(3.721)v$
    (B) $69.555 \pm (2.819)(3.721)$
    (C) $69.555 \pm (18.69)(3.721)$
    (D) $0.264 \pm (2.807)(0.109)$
    (E) $0.264 \pm (2.819)(0.109)$

Answer

39. Every afternoon, Jennifer waits for a subway train. The density curve for the amount of time she has to wait (in minutes) is shown in the diagram below.

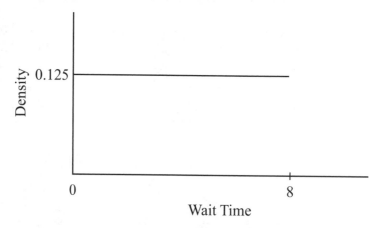

The mean and standard deviation of the wait time are 4 and 2.309, respectively. If a random sample of 40 afternoons is taken, what is the approximate probability that Jennifer's sample mean wait time is less than 5 minutes?

(A) 0.003
(B) 0.332
(C) 0.625
(D) 0.668
(E) 0.997

Answer

40. Two variables, x and y, were measured for a random sample of 10 subjects. In the first of two transformations, log y was plotted (on the vertical axis) against x (on the horizontal axis), a least squares regression was performed on the transformed variables, and the following residual plot was obtained.

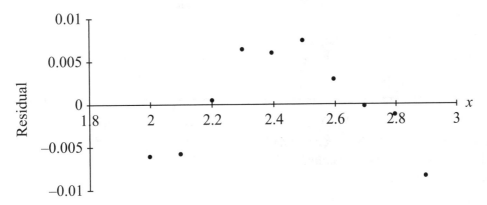

In the second transformation, log y was plotted (on the vertical axis) against log x (on the horizontal axis), a least squares regression was performed on the transformed variables, and the following residual plot was obtained.

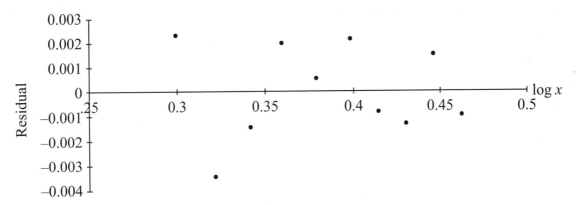

Which of the following conclusions is best supported by the evidence above?

(A) x and y are related according to an equation of the form $y = ax^p$, where a and p are constants.

(B) x and y are related according to an equation of the form $y = a + x^p$, where a and p are constants.

(C) x and y are related according to an equation of the form $y = a \cdot b^x$, where a and b are constants.

(D) x and y are related according to an equation of the form $y = a + b^x$, where a and b are constants.

(E) x and y are related according to an equation of the form $y = a + b \log x$, where a and b are constants.

Answer

SECTION II
Part A
Questions 1–5
Spend about 65 minutes on this part of the exam.
Percent of Section II grade—75

Directions: Show all your work. Indicate clearly the methods you use, because you will be graded on the correctness of your method as well as on the accuracy and completeness of your results and explanations.

1. For several years, Ellen has been recording music onto audio cassettes. Having accumulated 81 cassettes in this way, she has recently had all of them transferred to digital format, with each cassette going over to one computer file. The sizes of these 81 files in megabytes (MB) are summarized in the table below.

N	MEAN	MEDIAN	STDEV	SE MEAN	MIN	MAX	Q1	Q3
81	544.78	566	167.26	18.58	99	774	463	667.5

(a) Are there any outliers in this data set? Show clearly the method you use to answer this question.

(b) Based on the information given, do you think that the distribution of the file sizes is skewed to the right, skewed to the left, or roughly symmetrical? Explain your answer.

170

(c) Approximately what percent of the computer files have sizes between 463 and 667.5 megabytes? Explain.

(d) The standard deviation is given as 167.26. Explain how this value summarizes the variability of the file sizes.

2. A driver is interested in buying a new car of a particular type, and she wants to find out how the value of the car is likely to change in its first few years. She randomly selects 20 used cars of this type that are for sale and are at least one year and at most three years old, and notes for each its age (in years) and its price (in dollars). She then uses a computer to fit a least squares regression line to the data. Part of the computer output is shown below.

```
Dependent variable: Price

Predictor          Coef      SE Coef        T           P
Constant     25844.789     1073.413     24.08     <.0001
Age          -4764.155      526.3235     -9.05     <.0001

S = 1498.81      R-sq = 82.0%      R-sq (adj) = 81.0%
```

(a) What is the value of the correlation coefficient for age and price? Interpret this correlation.

(b) State the equation of the regression line and interpret its slope in the context of this question.

(c) State and interpret the value of the intercept of the regression line. Can this value be usefully applied to the prices of this type of car?

When the driver used the computer to fit the least squares regression line to the data, the computer also displayed the residual plot shown below.

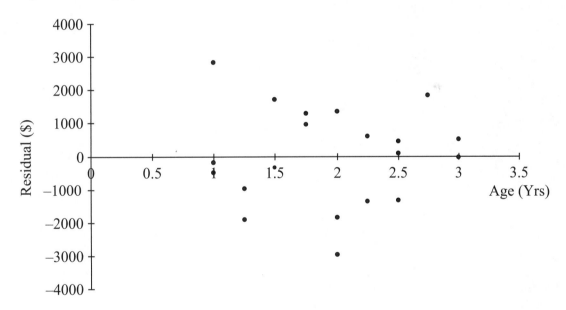

(d) What does the residual plot tell you about the appropriateness of using the least squares regression line to model the prices of cars of this type that are at least one year and at most three years old? Explain.

3. An investor is trying to decide between two mutual funds, Fund A and Fund B. The investor consults an economist, who estimates that for either of the two funds the amount of money gained in any given month on a $1000 dollar investment is approximately normally distributed, and that the gain or loss in any month can be considered to be independent of the gain or loss in any other month. Moreover, the economist estimates that, if the current economic climate continues, the monthly gains on $1000 in the two funds have the expected values (means) and standard deviations given in the table below.

Gain in dollars on a $1000 investment

	Expected Value	Standard Deviation
Fund A	4	5
Fund B	4	18

Assume throughout this question that the current economic climate continues.

(a) Explain why the investor might choose Fund A over Fund B.

(b) In any given month, what is the probability that Fund A gains money?

(c) What is the probability that Fund A gains money in exactly two of the next four months?

(d) A different investor decides to invest $8000 in Fund A and $3000 in Fund B. Assuming that the amounts gained by the two funds are independent, what are the mean and the standard deviation of the amount gained by this investment in the first month?

4. A company is developing a new treatment for gloves worn by gymnasts. The hope is that this treatment will more effectively prevent wear on the gloves than the treatment in use for gloves currently on the market. The company will recruit 50 male gymnasts as volunteers who will wear the gloves as they usually would for six months.

An employee at the company suggests an experimental design whereby the 50 gymnasts would be randomly assigned to two groups of 25. One group would be given gloves with the new treatment and the other would be given gloves with the current treatment. At the end of the study the wear on the gloves with the new treatment would be compared to the wear on the gloves with the current treatment.

(a) How would you assign the 50 gymnasts to the two groups of 25 for a completely randomized design?

(b) Why would the groups be assigned randomly rather than, for example, allowing some of the gymnasts to choose which group they would be in?

The company employs a statistician who suggests a different experimental design. Each of the gymnasts will be given a pair of gloves of which one glove has been treated with the new treatment and the other has been treated with the current treatment. For each gymnast it will be randomly decided whether it is the left glove or the right glove that receives the new treatment.

(c) Explain why this second experimental design is preferable to the first.

5. An experiment was designed to determine whether, in a test of physical endurance, the presence of other participants improved performance. The 32 students in a high school class were randomly assigned to two groups: Group 1 and Group 2. Each student was asked to hold a weight at arm's length in his or her dominant hand for as long as possible. The time (in seconds) for which each student was able to continue to hold the weight in this way was noted. (The same weight was used for each student, and care was taken to ensure that the students' arms were straight, and held in a horizontal position to the side of the body.) Each student in Group 1 performed the task with only the time recorder present. When students in Group 2 performed the task, the other students in Group 2 remained in the room and were allowed to give encouragement to the person performing the task.

The following results were obtained.

Group 1	180	128	135	207	120	207	159	187	183	83	53	154	72	128	105	227
Group 2	278	126	258	280	225	216	166	138	177	162	301	199	76	390	145	384

Does the presence of other participants appear to bring about a higher mean time for this task? Give appropriate statistical evidence to support your conclusion.

Spend about 25 minutes on this part of the exam.
Percent of Section II grade—25

Directions: Show all your work. Indicate clearly the methods you use, because you will be graded on the correctness of your method as well as on the accuracy and completeness of your results and explanations.

6. A Board of Education is considering changing the schedule at its two high schools, Central and Northern, so that the school day will start and end one hour later than it does currently. In order to get an idea of student attitudes about the idea, the Board instructs each school to perform a survey on a small sample of its student body.

    (a) The administration of Central High School selects a random sample of 40 students at the school and asks each student in the sample whether or not he/she is in favor of the idea. Twenty-six of the students respond that they are in favor, and the remaining 14 students respond that they are not in favor. Perform a test to determine whether this result provides evidence that a majority of the students at Central High School are in favor of the idea.

The administration of Northern High School decides to include in its survey the possibility of "No Opinion." It designs the following survey question.

> "The school day should start and end one hour later."
>
> Disagree (D)_____   No opinion (N)_____   Agree (A) _____

The administration decides that a "D" will score 0, an "N" will score 1, and an "A" will score 2. Having administered the survey to a random sample of 20 students, the administration adds up the scores and finds a total score of 24. An assistant is now given the job of using simulation in order to facilitate a decision as to whether this result reflects support for the idea amongst the student body of Northern High School as a whole. Parts (b), (c), and (d) of this question are concerned with this process.

(b) Suppose that the three responses are favored by equal proportions of students at Northern High School. How would you assign digits in a random number table to simulate the responses to this survey?

(c) Use the random number table given below and your assignment of digits from part (b) to simulate the responses from one sample of 20 students. Show your work clearly on the table, and note the total score for your sample.

4	4	7	3	8	8	5	3	5	1	7	7	6	7	8
6	3	7	6	4	2	5	9	3	9	5	3	8	8	9
6	6	4	8	5	2	5	2	9	9	4	6	9	8	8
1	6	9	0	9	9	0	1	0	4	9	7	4	8	0

The assistant runs the simulation in part (c) 200 times, and obtains the following results.

Total Score	10	11	12	13	14	15	16	17	18	19	20	21	22	23	24	25	26	27	28	29	30
Number of Runs	1	3	4	3	8	9	16	13	26	11	17	15	28	16	15	6	5	2	0	1	1

(d) On the basis of this set of results (which is based on the assumption that the three responses are favored by equal proportions of the school), do you think that a total score of 24 in a sample of 20 students gives convincing evidence that the student body as a whole is in favor of the idea? Explain carefully the logic behind your answer.

Sample Examination Four

SECTION I
Time—1 hour and 30 minutes
Number of questions—40
Percent of total grade—50

Directions: Solve each of the following problems, using the available space for scratch work. Decide which is the best of the choices given and fill in the corresponding oval on the answer sheet. No credit will be given for anything written in the test book. Do not spend too much time on any one problem.

1. There are 24 people who work in a particular office. Their travel times (in minutes) from home to work are listed below.

    30 35 35 39 40 44 47 48 49 50 50 50 54 55 56 56 57 58 59 59 62 62 63 66

    Which of the following is closest to the 20th percentile travel time (in minutes) for these 24 people?

    (A) 30   (B) 40   (C) 50   (D) 60   (E) 70

Answer

182

2. A young basketball player estimates that he is successful on one in every three free throws. He wishes to simulate a sequence of free throws using a table of random digits, and he is willing to assume that the results of the throws are independent of each other. Of the following, which would be the best strategy to use?

(A) Take one digit at a time, and have 0–2 represent success and 3–9 represent failure
(B) Take one digit at a time, and have 0–2 represent success, 3–8 represent failure, and ignore 9's
(C) Take two digits at a time, and have 00–32 represent success and 33–99 represent failure
(D) Take two digits at a time, and have 00–29 represent success and 30–99 represent failure
(E) Take three digits at a time, and have 000–333 represent success and 334–999 represent failure

Answer

3. The director of a company wants to know the mean salary of all the company's employees. The most effective way of determining this is to

(A) record the salaries of a simple random sample of employees
(B) record the salaries of a stratified random sample of employees
(C) record the salaries of a cluster sample of employees
(D) record the salaries of a convenience sample of employees
(E) consult computer records regarding the salaries of all employees

Answer

4. Suppose that a study of 500 randomly chosen teenagers established that those who had regularly played video games over the previous year tended to have a greater susceptibility to apathy (lack of motivation) than those who had not regularly played video games. Of the following, which would be the best way to establish whether regular playing of video games by teenagers <u>causes</u> apathy?

   (A) Repeat the study, this time stratifying by gender
   (B) Repeat the study, this time making sure that all ages between 13 and 19, inclusive, are covered adequately
   (C) Repeat the study, this time increasing the sample size to 1000 teenagers
   (D) Repeat the study, this time making sure that all types of video game are used
   (E) Perform a study using 50 teenagers. Randomly choose which 25 will play video games regularly and which 25 will not, and observe any connection between video game playing and apathy

Answer

5. In a large company, it has been assumed for several years that approximately 65% of the employees regularly eat the lunches provided by the company. However, it is now suspected that this figure has increased. In order to test this, a random sample of 50 employees is selected, and it is found that 36 of them regularly eat the lunches provided. If a significance test is to be performed, and the proportion of all employees who regularly eat the meals is to be denoted by p, what are the null and alternative hypotheses that should be used?

   (A) $H_0: p = 0.72$; $H_a: p < 0.72$
   (B) $H_0: p = 0.72$; $H_a: p > 0.72$
   (C) $H_0: p = 0.65$; $H_a: p = 0.72$
   (D) $H_0: p = 0.65$; $H_a: p < 0.65$
   (E) $H_0: p = 0.65$; $H_a: p > 0.65$

Answer

6. The sugar level and the protein level were measured for each animal in a sample of bulls. A scatterplot was drawn with sugar level plotted on the horizontal (x) axis and protein level plotted on the vertical (y) axis. The coefficient of determination, r^2, between these two variables was found to be 0.81. Of the following, which is the best interpretation of this value of r^2?

(A) 81% of the variation in protein levels can be explained by the least squares regression line relating protein level and sugar level.

(B) 81% of the variation in protein levels and sugar levels can be explained by the least squares regression line relating protein level and sugar level.

(C) 81% of the protein levels can be explained by the least squares regression line relating protein level and sugar level.

(D) 81% of the sugar levels can be explained by the least squares regression line relating protein level and sugar level.

(E) 81% of the relationship between sugar level and protein level can be explained by the least squares regression line.

Answer

7. In a study, 12 subjects were required to perform a task with their dominant hand and the same task with their non-dominant hand. The following results were obtained:

Subject	1	2	3	4	5	6	7	8	9	10	11	12
Time with Dominant Hand (seconds)	30	20	24	17	26	27	19	22	18	24	22	33
Time with non-Dominant Hand (seconds)	34	23	26	16	28	27	21	25	20	28	26	40

Assuming that the conditions for inference are met, which of the following significance tests could legitimately be used to analyze this dataset?

   I.   Two-sample t-test
  II.   Paired t-test
 III. t-test for the slope of the regression line

(A) I only
(B) II only
(C) I and II only
(D) II and III only
(E) I, II, and III

Answer

8. A cube with faces numbered 1 through 6 is rolled 5 times. What is the probability that the number of sixes rolled is either 1 or 2?

    (A) 0.093   (B) 0.161   (C) 0.482   (D) 0.563   (E) 0.965

Answer

9. A statistician takes a simple random sample of size 15 from a very large population whose standard deviation is unknown. The statistician's intention is to perform a one-sample t-test for the mean. A boxplot of the sample values is drawn, and it is found that the distribution of the sample values is roughly symmetrical and that there are no outliers. The statistician is now justified in using the t-test because

    (A) the boxplot has shown that the sample is large enough for use of the t-distribution
    (B) it is known that the sample is t-distributed
    (C) it is known that the population is t-distributed
    (D) it is known that the sample is normally distributed
    (E) it is feasible that the population is normally distributed

Answer

10. A set of 23 measurements is summarized by the following boxplot.

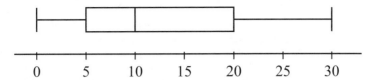

Which of the following could be the mean of the 23 measurements?

(A) 7   (B) 9   (C) 12   (D) 22   (E) 27

Answer

11. A study is carried out to compare the effectiveness of two types of fertilizer, A and B. 260 seeds of a particular plant are randomly assigned to the two types of fertilizer. Of the 120 seeds assigned to fertilizer A, 83 are found to germinate, and of the 140 seeds assigned to fertilizer B, 78 are found to germinate. Which of the following is a 99% confidence interval for $p_A - p_B$, the difference between the two proportions of all seeds germinating for the two types of fertilizer?

(A) $\left(\dfrac{83}{120} - \dfrac{78}{140}\right) \pm 2.326\sqrt{\dfrac{(83/120)(37/120)}{120} + \dfrac{(78/140)(62/140)}{140}}$

(B) $\left(\dfrac{83}{120} - \dfrac{78}{140}\right) \pm 2.326\sqrt{\dfrac{(83/120)(78/140)}{120} + \dfrac{(37/120)(62/140)}{140}}$

(C) $\left(\dfrac{83}{120} - \dfrac{78}{140}\right) \pm 2.326\sqrt{\dfrac{161}{120} \cdot \dfrac{99}{260}\left(\dfrac{1}{120} + \dfrac{1}{140}\right)}$

(D) $\left(\dfrac{83}{120} - \dfrac{78}{140}\right) \pm 2.576\sqrt{\dfrac{(83/120)(37/120)}{120} + \dfrac{(78/140)(62/140)}{140}}$

(E) $\left(\dfrac{83}{120} - \dfrac{78}{140}\right) \pm 2.576\sqrt{\dfrac{161}{260} \cdot \dfrac{99}{260}\left(\dfrac{1}{120} + \dfrac{1}{140}\right)}$

Answer

12. In a particular state, a polling organization wishes to find out whether there is a difference in political preference between the over-forties and the under-forties. A random sample of people over the age of forty will be taken, and a random sample of people under the age of forty will be taken. Each person will be asked whether he/she supports the Democrats, the Republicans, or some other party. Of the following, which would be the most appropriate significance test to analyze the results of the study? You may assume that the conditions for inference are met.

   (A) One-proportion z-test
   (B) Two-sample t-test for the difference of two means
   (C) Paired t-test for the difference of two means
   (D) Chi-square test for goodness of fit
   (E) Chi-square test for homogeneity

Answer

13. A marketing company is interested in finding out whether telephone salespeople would perform better if they did relaxation or stretching exercises before they start their work. A set of salespeople will be randomly assigned to three groups. For a few minutes before they start work, the salespeople in the first group will do relaxation exercises, the salespeople in the second group will do stretching exercises, and the salespeople in the third group will be given some free time. The sales performances of the people in the three groups will then be compared. In the context of this experiment, which of the following is an instance of replication?

   (A) Using a set of salespeople that represents the population of interest
   (B) Making sure that the sales portion of the experience is the same for the three groups
   (C) Making sure that the groups contain roughly equal numbers of experienced salespeople and inexperienced salespeople
   (D) Using a large enough number of salespeople so that any differences between the groups (in terms of the people assigned) become negligible
   (E) Getting a result for the experiment that is correct for the population of interest

Answer

14. Of the distributions represented by the histograms below, which has the smallest standard deviation?

(A)
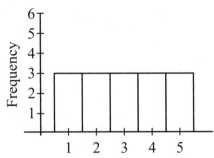

(B)
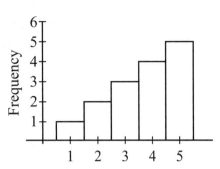

(C)
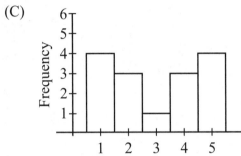

(D)
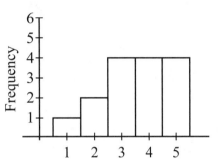

(E)
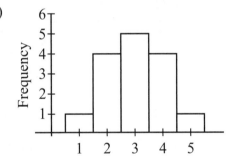

Answer

15. A college offers two courses in calculus: Calculus 1 and Calculus 2. Last semester, 60.9% of calculus students took Calculus 1 and the rest took Calculus 2. (No student took both courses.) Of the students who took Calculus 1, 28.0% received A's, and of the students who took Calculus 2, 38.1% received A's. If a student is selected at random from those who received A's in calculus, what is the probability that the student took Calculus 1?

(A) 0.170   (B) 0.280   (C) 0.534   (D) 0.609   (E) 0.720

Answer

16. A large number of students at a high school take an Algebra II course that emphasizes calculator use. The chairman of the math department is concerned that students' mental arithmetic skills might be declining through lack of practice during the course. He selects a random sample of students who take the course and gives them a mental arithmetic test (scored out of 30) at the beginning of the course (PreTest) and a comparable test at the end of the course (PostTest). The computer output shown below gives the results of a test of $H_0 : \mu_D = 0$ *versus* $H_a : \mu_D < 0$, where D denotes the difference in scores (PostTest − PreTest).

```
                      Matched Pairs
               Difference: PostTest - PreTest

PreTest Mean        28.4286    t-Ratio        -2.065591
PostTest Mean       27.2857    DF                    13
Mean Difference     -1.14286   Prob < t          0.0297
Std Error           0.55328
N                         14
Correlation         0.8251
```

Assuming that the conditions for inference are met, which of the following is the best conclusion that can be drawn from the analysis?

(A) There is evidence at the 5% level (but not the 1% level) that on average the students' mental arithmetic abilities have increased.

(B) There is evidence at the 1% level that on average the students' mental arithmetic abilities have increased.

(C) There is evidence at the 5% level that there has been a change in the students' average mental arithmetic ability.

(D) There is evidence at the 5% level (but not the 1% level) that on average the students' mental arithmetic abilities have decreased.

(E) There is evidence at the 1% level that on average the students' mental arithmetic abilities have decreased.

Answer

17. A very large population has mean μ and standard deviation σ. A random sample of size n (where n is at least 2) is to be taken from the population. The sample mean will be denoted by $\bar{x}$. Which of the following is NOT known to be true?

    (A) The mean of all the possible values of $\bar{x}$ is μ.

    (B) The standard deviation of the sample is $\dfrac{\sigma}{\sqrt{n}}$.

    (C) If n is large, the distribution of all possible values of $\bar{x}$ is approximately normal.

    (D) The larger the sample, the smaller the standard deviation of all the possible values of $\bar{x}$.

    (E) The standard deviation of all the possible values of $\bar{x}$ is less than σ.

Answer

18. The scores on a math test are said to be negatively skewed (skewed to the left). Which of the following is the best interpretation of this statement?

    (A) The spread of the scores below the median is greater than the spread of the scores above the median.
    (B) The spread of the scores above the median is greater than the spread of the scores below the median.
    (C) When a histogram of the scores is drawn, the highest point in the histogram is towards the left of the distribution.
    (D) There are more low scores than high scores.
    (E) There are more high scores than low scores.

Answer

19. The students in a statistics class participated in an activity concerning the value of a particular population parameter. An observational study was conducted, and then the results of the study were analyzed by means of a significance test involving the null hypothesis H_0. After the analysis was completed, the teacher, who knew the true value of the parameter, announced (correctly) that a Type II error had occurred.

Which of the following can NOT be concluded from the information given?

(A) The study was conducted poorly.
(B) The significance test failed to reach a correct conclusion.
(C) H_0 was false.
(D) H_0 was not rejected.
(E) A Type I error did not occur.

Answer

20. A study is conducted to compare the effects of aerobic and anaerobic exercise on the production of a particular growth hormone. Forty volunteer teenagers with slowed growth are randomly assigned to two groups. The teenagers in the first group are supervised doing aerobic exercise and the teenagers in the second group are supervised doing anaerobic exercise. The levels of the growth hormone in the volunteers are measured at the beginning and at the end of the study. Is the study an experiment or an observational study?

(A) It is an experiment because the teenagers used did not form a random sample.
(B) It is an experiment because the teenagers were made to exercise in particular ways.
(C) It is an experiment because the hormone levels were measured before and after the exercise.
(D) It is an observational study because there is no control group.
(E) It is an observational study because the teenagers were observed exercising.

Answer

21. There is a standard weight in ounces for squash balls. A machine produces squash balls whose weights are normally distributed. The machine is adjusted so that the mean weight of the balls produced is the standard weight. To the nearest one thousandth, what should be the standard deviation of the weights of the balls produced by the machine so that 98% of the balls have weights that are within 0.2 ounce of the standard weight?

(A) 0.086 ounce
(B) 0.097 ounce
(C) 0.372 ounce
(D) 0.408 ounce
(E) 0.602 ounce

Answer

22. For a random sample of 20 salamanders, the slope of the regression line for predicting weights from lengths is found to be 4.169, and the standard error of this estimate is found to be 2.142. When performing a test of H_0: $\beta = 0$ against H_a: $\beta \neq 0$, where β is the slope of the regression line for the population of salamanders, the t-value is

(A) 0.435   (B) 0.514   (C) 1.946   (D) 8.258   (E) 8.704

Answer

23. In the context of an observational study, which of the following is most appropriate as an instance of bias?

   (A) Getting a sample that over-emphasizes some characteristic of the population that is relevant to the study

   (B) Designing a sampling method that is likely to result in a sample that will over-emphasize some characteristic of the population that is relevant to the study

   (C) Wrongly interpreting an association between two characteristics as the causation of one by the other

   (D) Getting a false conclusion to the study

   (E) Revealing a prejudiced attitude amongst the population

Answer

24. A customer at a supermarket buys 11 items. The prices (in dollars) of the items are summarized in the table below.

Mean	3.4572727
Std Dev	1.6129916
Std Err Mean	0.4863353
upper 95% Mean	4.5408952
lower 95% Mean	2.3736502
N	11
Min	1.4900
Q1	2.5000
Median	2.9900
Q3	4.6600
Max	7.1300

The z-score for one of the items is -0.290. What is the price of this item?

(A) $2.84   (B) $2.99   (C) $3.32   (D) $3.37   (E) $3.93

Answer

25. A random sample of size 15 is taken from a population, and a 95% confidence interval for the population mean is calculated, from the sample data, to be (64.06, 66.96). Of the following, which gives the best interpretation of 95% confidence in this context?

    (A) If many random samples of size 15 from this population are taken, then 95% of the time the population mean will be within the interval (64.06, 66.96).
    (B) If many random samples of size 15 from this population are taken, then 95% of the time the sample mean will be within the interval (64.06, 66.96).
    (C) If many random samples of size 15 from this population are taken and the confidence intervals are calculated in the same way, then 95% of the confidence intervals will contain the population mean.
    (D) If many random samples of size 15 from this population are taken and the confidence intervals are calculated in the same way, then 95% of the confidence intervals will contain the sample mean.
    (E) 95% of the population measurements lie within the interval (64.06, 66.96).

Answer

26. Terry is standing in line waiting for a snack. He will receive one serving of chips and one serving of salsa. The amount of chips (in grams) per serving is a random variable with standard deviation 3.7. The amount of salsa (in grams) per serving is a random variable with standard deviation 2.8. The chips contain 5 calories per gram and the salsa contains 0.5 calories per gram. The amounts of the two snacks that Terry receives can be considered to be independent. What is the standard deviation (in grams) of the total number of calories Terry receives?

    (A) 4.46   (B) 8.51   (C) 18.55   (D) 19.90   (E) 344.21

Answer

27. A spelling quiz is taken by 12 girls and 20 boys. The mean score for the girls is 8.25 and the mean score for the boys is 7.3. Of the following, which is closest to the mean score for all of the students?

    (A) 7.66   (B) 7.71   (C) 7.76   (D) 7.78   (E) 7.89

Answer

28. Four cubes, each with faces numbered 1 through 6, are rolled. To the nearest one-thousandth, what is the probability that the largest of the four scores is a six?

    (A) 0.096   (B) 0.386   (C) 0.518   (D) 0.668   (E) 0.783

Answer

29. The manager of a clothing store selects a random sample of 30 items of clothing that have been returned to the store. For each item in the sample the manager determines whether the item has been worn (W) or has not been worn (N). The following results are obtained.

W N N N N W W N N W W W W W W

W W N N N N W W N W W W N W W

A significance test is to be conducted in order to determine whether these results provide convincing evidence that a majority of items returned to the store have been worn. Which of the following is closest to the p-value for the test?

(A) 0.032   (B) 0.137   (C) 0.264   (D) 0.273   (E) 0.282

Answer

30. Max randomly selects a sample of five students from his math class, and asks each student in the sample how many phones he/she has at home. Having calculated the sample mean number of phones, $\overline{x}$, Max finds, for each student in the sample, the squared deviation, $(x - \overline{x})^2$. The squared deviations are listed below.

$$(x - \overline{x})^2$$
3.24
3.24
17.64
0.04
0.64

What is the standard deviation of the number of phones for this sample of five students?

(A) 2.23   (B) 2.49   (C) 4.96   (D) 6.20   (E) 7.24

Answer

31. Let X be the score when a cube with faces numbered 1 through 6 is rolled. You are given that $\mu_X = 3.5$ and $\sigma_X = 1.708$.

    A cube with faces numbered 1 through 6 is rolled 50 times. Which of the following most closely approximates the probability that the total score is at least 200?

    (A) 0.000   (B) 0.019   (C) 0.385   (D) 0.483   (E) 0.500

    Answer

32. The owner of a machine that makes ball bearings wishes to estimate the mean weight of all ball bearings made by the machine. The standard deviation of the weights of all ball bearings made by the machine is known. The owner at first intends to use a 95% confidence interval based on a sample of 50 ball bearings, but then decides to use a 95% confidence interval based on a sample of 200 ball bearings. Which of the following is true?

    (A) The width of the second confidence interval will be 4 times the width of the first confidence interval.
    (B) The width of the second confidence interval will be twice the width of the first confidence interval.
    (C) The width of the second confidence interval will be half the width of the first confidence interval.
    (D) The width of the second confidence interval will be a quarter of the width of the first confidence interval.
    (E) The width of the second confidence interval will be one sixteenth of the width of the first confidence interval.

    Answer

33. For a group of 15 male students the mean height is 70.2 inches and the mean weight is 160.3 pounds. The slope of the least squares regression line for predicting weights from heights is 2.75. What does the regression line predict for the weight of a student whose height is 68 inches?

    (A) 154.25 pounds
    (B) 159.5 pounds
    (C) 161.1 pounds
    (D) 166.35 pounds
    (E) 187 pounds

Answer

34. A random sample of 25 students at a large college is taken. The IQ of each student is measured by two different methods, Method A and Method B. A regression analysis is performed, and part of the computer output is shown below.

Dependent variable: MethodB				
Predictor	Coef	SE Coef	T	P
Constant	74.949887	20.88781	3.59	0.0016
MethodA	0.3409875	0.195475	1.74	0.0944

A test of the following hypotheses is performed:

H_0: There is no correlation between the results of Method A and Method B (true slope = 0)

H_a: There is a correlation between the results of Method A and Method B (true slope ≠ 0)

Assuming that conditions for inference are met and using a 5% significance level, which of the following is a correct conclusion to the test?

    (A) We have sufficient evidence to conclude that there is a nonzero correlation between the results of the two methods.
    (B) We do not have sufficient evidence to conclude that there is a nonzero correlation between the results of the two methods.
    (C) We have sufficient evidence to conclude that there is no correlation between the results of the two methods.
    (D) We either do or do not have sufficient evidence to conclude that there is a nonzero correlation between the results of the two methods, according to which part of the table we use.
    (E) No information regarding correlation can be inferred from the computer output.

Answer

35. Which of the following distributions is NOT symmetrical?

    (A) The chi-square distribution with 8 degrees of freedom
    (B) The t-distribution with 8 degrees of freedom
    (C) The normal distribution with mean 52 and standard deviation 6
    (D) The binomial distribution with $n = 43$ and $p = 0.5$
    (E) The distribution of the score when a cube with faces numbered 1 through 6 is rolled

Answer

36. An experiment is performed to measure the effectiveness of a new drug designed to encourage weight loss. The drug is in the form of a tablet. Forty volunteer overweight adults are randomly assigned to two groups, A and B, each with 20 people. The people in Group A are told to take the drug on a regular basis, and otherwise to go about their lives in the normal way. The people in Group B are simply told to go about their lives in the normal way, and are given no medication. After a month, the weight loss for each experimental subject is recorded. (If someone has gained weight then the weight loss is recorded as a negative number.) Throughout the experiment, each experimental subject is completely unaware of the other experimental subjects.

It is found that the people in Group A undergo a significantly greater weight loss on average than the people in Group B.

According to one of the experimenters, this result gives evidence that the chemical in the drug is effective in encouraging weight loss. Of the following, which provides the strongest argument against this claim?

    (A) Twenty is not a large enough number of people to give evidence of the effectiveness of the drug.
    (B) The people in Group A might have just been eating less than the people in Group B.
    (C) The weight loss of the people in Group A could be attributed to the psychological factor of taking a tablet.
    (D) The loss of weight could have been brought about by the warmer weather during the month of the experiment and the fact that this encourages increased exercise.
    (E) Some of the people in Group A might not have taken the tablets.

Answer

37. Independent samples from two populations are taken, and a t-statistic is used to test the null hypothesis H_0: $\mu_1 = \mu_2$ against the alternative H_a: $\mu_1 > \mu_2$. The resulting p-value is 0.043. Using the same samples, a (two-sided) confidence interval will now be constructed for $\mu_1 - \mu_2$. Of the following, which is the smallest confidence level for which the confidence interval will contain zero?

(A) 90% confidence
(B) 92% confidence
(C) 94% confidence
(D) 96% confidence
(E) 98% confidence

Answer

38. In a listing of 42 houses available for rent, for each house the size (in hundreds of square feet) and the monthly rent (in dollars) is given. A scatterplot is constructed with house size on the horizontal axis and monthly rent on the vertical axis, and a linear regression analysis is run. The computer output is shown below.

```
                Dependent variable: Rent

Predictor          Coef        SE Coef         T          P
Constant        602.50858     88.29774       6.82    <.0001
Size            24.926936      3.686165      6.76    <.0001

S = 165.62    R-sq = 53.3%    R-sq (adj) = 52.2%
```

The size of one of the houses (in hundreds of square feet) is 32, and the monthly rent is $1450. Which of the following (in dollars) is closest to the residual for this house?

(A) −90   (B) −70   (C) −50   (D) 50   (E) 70

Answer

39. In a large country, the heights of the men are normally distributed with mean 70 inches and standard deviation 3 inches. A recruitment agency considers a man suitable for physical labor if his height is between 67 inches and 76 inches. A man is chosen at random from the set of all men who satisfy this condition. What is the probability that this man is less than 70 inches tall?

(A) 0.341   (B) 0.417   (C) 0.5   (D) 0.683   (E) 0.715

Answer

40. A spinner has four sectors, labeled 1, 2, 3, and 4, respectively. Each spin results in one of the four sectors being selected. The spinner is spun 120 times, and the number of 1's is denoted by f_1, the number of 2's is denoted by f_2, the number of 3's is denoted by f_3, and the number of 4's is denoted by f_4.

Let p be the probability that

$$\frac{(f_1 - 30)^2}{30} + \frac{(f_2 - 30)^2}{30} + \frac{(f_3 - 30)^2}{30} + \frac{(f_4 - 30)^2}{30}$$

is greater than 6.25.

Given that the four outcomes on the spinner are equally likely, which of the following is closest to the value of p?

(A) 0.1   (B) 0.2   (C) 0.3   (D) 0.4   (E) 0.5

Answer

SECTION II
Part A
Questions 1–5
Spend about 65 minutes on this part of the exam.
Percent of Section II grade—75

Directions: Show all your work. Indicate clearly the methods you use, because you will be graded on the correctness of your method as well as on the accuracy and completeness of your results and explanations.

1. The cumulative relative frequency graph shown below represents the ages of the residents of a country.

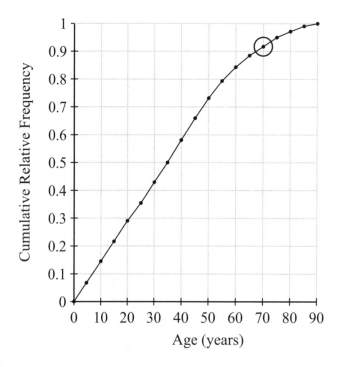

(a) What information is conveyed by the circled point?

(b) The total number of residents of the country is 32,465,233. Calculate an estimate of the number of residents who are at least 40 years old.

(c) What is the interquartile range of the ages of the residents?

(d) Between 0 and 50 on the horizontal axis, the graph is approximately a straight line. Explain the relevance of this.

2. Every ten years since 1920, a magazine has announced to the public its number of subscribers. These numbers are given in the table below.

Year	Years since 1920	Number of Subscribers
1920	0	1443
1930	10	11341
1940	20	9436
1950	30	17450
1960	40	45907
1970	50	91747
1980	60	77139
1990	70	435492
2000	80	1178498

A regression analysis is performed using <u>Years since 1920</u> as the independent variable and <u>log(number of subscribers)</u> as the dependent variable, where log denotes the logarithm function with base 10. The following computer output and residual plot are obtained.

```
Predictor          Coef        SE Coef            T           P
Constant       3.364928       0.140197        24.00     <.0001
Yrs since      0.0315783      0.002945        10.72     <.0001
1920

S = 0.228     R-sq = 94.3%      R-sq (adj) = 93.4%
```

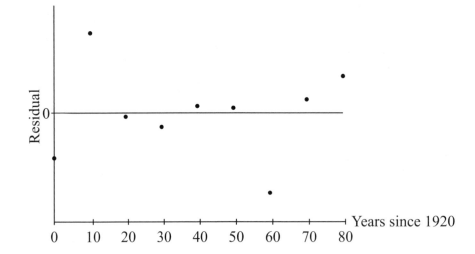

(a) Comment on the appropriateness of this linear regression for modeling the relationship between log(number of subscribers) and Years since 1920.

(b) What is the equation of the least squares regression line that describes the relationship between <u>log(number of subscribers)</u> and <u>Years since 1920</u>?

3. A city government has recently increased the police presence on its streets. In order to find out whether there is opposition to this policy amongst city residents, a community action group will send out a survey to all residents asking for their agreement or disagreement with a simple statement. Once the responses have been received, the group will issue a press release quoting the level of opposition found in the responses as the level of opposition to the policy in the city as a whole.

(a) Describe one source of bias evident from the description of the survey given above and explain the likely effect of this bias on the result of the survey.

(b) Explain how the community action group might change the design of its survey in order to address the issue in part (a).

4. Six cards are labeled 1, 2, 2, 3, 3, 4, respectively. Considering this deck as the "population," the population mean is $\mu = 2.5$. Someone who does not know what numbers are written on the cards is going to take a random sample of four cards (without replacement), and will use either the sample mean or the sample midrange to estimate the population mean. (The midrange is defined as $\frac{\text{maximum} + \text{minimum}}{2}$.) We concern ourselves here with the choice of the mean or the midrange for this purpose.

We will start by writing the cards as {1, 2, 2*, 3, 3*, 4}, in order to distinguish the two 2's and the two 3's in the population.

(a) The table below lists all possible samples of size four, along with the value of the sample mean for each sample, and some values of the sample midrange.

Sample	Sample Mean	Sample Midrange
1, 2, 2*, 3	2	2
1, 2, 2*, 3*	2	2
1, 2, 2*, 4	2.25	2.5
1, 2, 3, 3*	2.25	
1, 2, 3, 4	2.5	
1, 2, 3*, 4	2.5	
1, 2*, 3, 3*	2.25	
1, 2*, 3, 4	2.5	
1, 2*, 3*, 4	2.5	
1, 3, 3*, 4	2.75	
2, 2*, 3, 3*	2.5	
2, 2*, 3, 4	2.75	
2, 2*, 3*, 4	2.75	
2, 3, 3*, 4	3	
2*, 3, 3*, 4	3	3

Complete the table by inserting the remaining values of the sample midrange.

(b) The probability distribution for the sample mean is given below.

Sample Mean	2	2.25	2.5	2.75	3
Probability	2/15	1/5	1/3	1/5	2/15

Construct the equivalent probability distribution for the sample midrange.

(c) Calculate the expected value of the sample mean and the expected value of the sample midrange.

(d) What does the expected value of the sample mean tell you about the appropriateness (or not) of using the sample mean for estimating the population mean?

What does the expected value of the sample midrange tell you about the appropriateness (or not) of using the sample midrange for estimating the population mean?

Explain your answers.

(e) You are given that the standard deviation of the sample mean is 0.303 and the standard deviation of the sample midrange is 0.365. As an estimator for the population mean, would you choose the statistic with the larger standard deviation or the statistic with the smaller standard deviation? Explain the reasoning behind this choice.

5. Michelle loves parakeets. (A *parakeet* is a type of parrot.) Working in a pet store, Michelle performed an experiment to compare male and female parakeets in their ability to mimic human speech. She repeatedly exposed each parakeet in the store to the phrase "I love you." She included 33 male and 44 female parakeets in her study. 14 of the male parakeets and 13 of the female parakeets were found to be successful in mimicking the phrase.

Suppose it is reasonable to assume that these sets of male and female parakeets were random samples from the populations of male and female parakeets. Do the results of Michelle's experiment give evidence of a difference between male and female parakeets in their ability to mimic speech? Provide a statistical justification to support your answer.

SECTION II
Part B
Question 6
Spend about 25 minutes on this part of the exam.
Percent of Section II grade—25

Directions: Show all your work. Indicate clearly the methods you use, because you will be graded on the correctness of your method as well as on the accuracy and completeness of your results and explanations.

6. The administration of a high school is concerned about grade inflation, and is planning a comparison of teachers in terms of their generosity with grades. (Teacher X is said to be more *generous* than Teacher Y if a student of a given ability is likely to get a higher grade from Teacher X than from Teacher Y.)

   (a) Consider a hypothetical situation where the same set of 12 math students is taught by two math teachers. Each teacher gives tests to the students during the year and awards grades at the end of the course. The grades received by the students are shown in the table below.

Student	1	2	3	4	5	6	7	8	9	10	11	12
Teacher X	99	94	88	80	83	84	82	82	82	91	90	65
Teacher Y	97	87	87	76	88	87	80	83	71	84	97	65

   Perform a test to determine whether the mean grade given by Teacher X is significantly higher than the mean grade given by Teacher Y.

If you need more room for your work for part (a), use the space below.

The problem for the administration is that it is very unusual for two teachers of a given subject to teach the same students. Consider two teachers, Teacher A and Teacher B, who both teach Precalculus. When a student signs up for Precalculus, he/she is assigned to either Teacher A or Teacher B, usually according to what other classes the student is taking. Teacher A has 64 Precalculus students and Teacher B has 67 Precalculus students. A two-sample t-test is performed in order to establish whether the mean grade given by Teacher A is significantly higher than the mean grade given by Teacher B. The computer output is shown below.

```
              Two Sample T for Teacher A vs Teacher B

                 N       Mean      StDev     SE Mean
Teacher A        64      85.02      7.57       0.90
Teacher B        67      82.25      6.87       0.70

Difference = μ Teacher A - μ Teacher B
Estimate for difference = 2.76
95% lower bound for difference: 0.67

T-Test of difference = 0 (vs >): T-value = 2.18
P-Value = 0.015 DF = 126.4
```

(b) What is the conclusion to the hypothesis test? Explain your reasoning, but do <u>not</u> carry out the complete test. (Use a significance level of 0.05.)

(c) Does your answer to part (b) imply that Teacher A is more generous than Teacher B?
     Explain.

In order to further compare Teacher A and Teacher B, scatterplots were constructed in which
the students' Precalculus grades were plotted against the students' average grades across all
subjects. The scatterplots for the students taught Precalculus by Teacher A and the students
taught Precalculus by Teacher B are shown below. The line $y = x$ has been added to both
scatterplots.

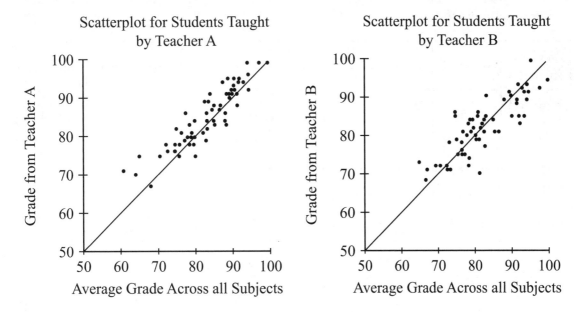

(d) Do the scatterplots provide any further information as to whether Teacher A is more
     generous than Teacher B? Explain your answer.

Sample Examination Five

SECTION I
Time—1 hour and 30 minutes
Number of questions—40
Percent of total grade—50

Directions: Solve each of the following problems, using the available space for scratch work. Decide which is the best of the choices given and fill in the corresponding oval on the answer sheet. No credit will be given for anything written in the test book. Do not spend too much time on any one problem.

1. A package delivery company keeps track of the weight of each package it handles. During a particular month, the company handles 14,532 packages. The weights of these packages are summarized in the following table:

Weight (pounds)	0 to < 5	5 to < 10	10 to < 20	20 to < 40	40 to < 60	60 to < 90	90 to < 120
Number of packages	3550	4215	2662	2219	887	555	444

Which of the following could be the 70th percentile package weight (in pounds) for that month?

(A) 6   (B) 19   (C) 42   (D) 48   (E) 84

Answer

2. Suppose that you are given a set of points, each with an x-coordinate and a y-coordinate. The points have been plotted on a graph. We can consider x to be the explanatory variable and y to be the response variable. The least squares regression line of y on x is the line that minimizes

(A) the sum of the horizontal distances of the points from the line
(B) the sum of the vertical distances of the points from the line
(C) the sum of the squares of the horizontal distances of the points from the line
(D) the sum of the squares of the vertical distances of the points from the line
(E) the sum of the squares of the perpendicular distances of the points from the line

Answer

3. A random number generator produces positive whole numbers between 1 and 5 inclusive. The five possible outcomes are equally likely. The random number generator will now be used to produce ten numbers. What is the probability that exactly four of these numbers will be less than 3?

(A) $\dbinom{10}{4}\left(\dfrac{2}{5}\right)^4\left(\dfrac{3}{5}\right)^6$

(B) $4\left(\dfrac{2}{5}\right)^4\left(\dfrac{3}{5}\right)^6$

(C) $\left(\dfrac{2}{5}\right)^4\left(\dfrac{3}{5}\right)^6$

(D) $\left(\dfrac{3}{5}\right)^3\left(\dfrac{2}{5}\right)$

(E) $\left(\dfrac{2}{5}\right)^4$

Answer

4. The board of directors of a health club is considering making changes to the club's facilities. As part of the decision-making process the board wishes to find out whether members of the club feel that improvements are necessary. The board asks the manager of the club to investigate, and the manager sends out a survey that asks the question, "Do you want to spend at least $10 million to renovate the facilities?" The survey is sent to all 820 members of the club, and 808 of them respond. Seventy-five percent of the respondents answer "No," and so the manager reports to the board that a majority of the membership is against making improvements.

   Of the following, which is the most likely source of bias in the study?

   (A) Some people included in the survey did not respond.
   (B) Some parts of the population of interest were not included in the study.
   (C) The question is worded in a way that is likely to influence the response.
   (D) The study makes use of a census, and so no sampling is involved.
   (E) The study does not make use of a stratified sample.

Answer

5. There are six students enrolled in an evening class. It has been estimated that, for any evening when the class meets, the probability distribution of the number of students who attend is as shown below.

Number of Students	0	1	2	3	4	5	6
Probability	0.05	0.15	0.16	0.18	0.22	0.16	0.08

   Suppose that, on a particular evening, it is known that at least two students are attending. What is the probability that, on that evening, at most four students are attending?

   (A) 0.34   (B) 0.43   (C) 0.56   (D) 0.70   (E) 0.76

Answer

6. One hundred subjects are to be assigned to two groups (Group 1 and Group 2) for an experiment that requires a completely randomized design. A method of randomization needs to be chosen that results in two groups of equal size. Which of the following methods is correct?

(A) For each subject, flip a coin. If the coin lands "heads," the subject is put into Group 1. If the coin lands "tails", the subject is put into Group 2.

(B) List the subjects in alphabetical order by name. Starting with the first subject, flip a coin. If the coin lands "heads," the subject is put into Group 1. If the coin lands "tails", the subject is put into Group 2. Continue in the same way until one of the groups contains 50 subjects. Then put the remaining subjects into the other group.

(C) List the subjects in alphabetical order by name. Using a table of random digits, assign a random four-digit number between 0001 and 9999 (inclusive) to each subject, ignoring four-digit numbers that have already been assigned. Those subjects with the 50 lowest four-digit numbers are assigned to Group 1. The remaining subjects are assigned to Group 2.

(D) Put the male subjects into Group 1 and the female subjects into Group 2.

(E) List the subjects in alphabetical order, and number the list 1 through 100. Those subjects with odd numbers are put into Group 1 and those with even numbers are put into Group 2.

Answer

---

7. Which of the following is NOT true?

(A) The mean is a measure of the center of a distribution.
(B) The median is a measure of the center of a distribution.
(C) The third (upper) quartile is a measure of the spread of a distribution.
(D) The standard deviation is a measure of the spread of a distribution.
(E) The range is a measure of the spread of a distribution.

Answer

---

8. Suppose that professional photographers generally use cameras made by manufacturer C, manufacturer N, or some other manufacturer. A photography magazine publishes an article that claims that research has been done and that particular percentages of the population of professional photographers fall into these three categories (C, N, and Other). One of the manufacturers doubts the figures published in the article, and so conducts its own research. The company takes a random sample of professional photographers, and finds out for each photographer what make of camera he/she uses. It then performs a chi-square goodness of fit test, using the null hypothesis that the magazine's claim is correct. The resulting chi-square statistic is 4.19, and a 5% significance level is used. Concerning the p-value and the conclusion for this test, which of the following is true?

(A) $p = 0.123$. We have convincing evidence at the 5% level that the magazine's claim is incorrect.

(B) $p = 0.123$. We do not have convincing evidence at the 5% level that the magazine's claim is incorrect.

(C) $p = 0.123$. We have convincing evidence at the 5% level that the magazine's claim is correct.

(D) $p = 0.242$. We do not have convincing evidence at the 5% level that the magazine's claim is incorrect.

(E) $p = 0.242$. We have convincing evidence at the 5% level that the magazine's claim is correct.

Answer

9. The counselor at a high school took a random sample of girls and a random sample of boys at the school and asked each student whether he or she had sought out extra help from a teacher during the previous five school days. The counselor wishes to investigate whether the data obtained provide convincing evidence that there is a difference between the proportion of girls at the school who would say they have sought out extra help during the previous five days and the proportion of boys at the school who would say they have sought out extra help during the previous five days. Of the following, which can NOT be part of the process of conducting a hypothesis test to investigate the counselor's question using a 0.01 level of significance?

(A) Checking that all four counts (the number of boys who say they have sought extra help, the number of boys who say they have not sought extra help, the number of girls who say they have sought extra help, and the number of girls who say they have not sought extra help) are large enough to justify using the inference procedure
(B) Assuming a normal distribution for a population
(C) Calculating a combined (pooled) sample proportion
(D) Using a z-statistic to carry out the test
(E) Given that the p-value is less than 0.01, rejecting the null hypothesis and concluding that there is convincing evidence of a difference between girls and boys in this regard

Answer

Questions 10-12 refer to the following scenario and computer output.

A student had access to rainfall and sunshine data for a particular location over a period of 60 years. She randomly selected a sample of 25 months from the 720 months available, and noted for each month in the sample the total rainfall (in millimeters) and the total sunshine (in hours). She then performed a regression analysis. Part of the computer output is shown below.

```
             Dependent variable: Sunshine
Predictor        Coef      SE Coef        T         P
Constant     248.98414    48.45664     5.14    <.0001
Rainfall      -1.67023    0.654083    -2.55    0.0178

S = 57.834   R-sq = 22.1%   R-sq (adj) = 18.7%
```

10. Which of the following is closest to the correlation between rainfall and sunshine for this data set?

   (A) -0.470 (B) -0.432 (C) 0.018 (D) 0.432 (E) 0.470

Answer

11. The computer output gives "S = 57.834". This value gives us an idea of the

   (A) slope of the regression line
   (B) variability of the rainfall values
   (C) variability of the sunshine values
   (D) variability of the rainfall values and the sunshine values
   (E) variability of the sunshine values from those predicted by the regression line

Answer

12. The regression analysis provided information about the regression line that can be used for predicting sunshine values from rainfall values using the data from the 25 months in the sample. The student now wishes to perform a significance test to determine whether these data provide convincing evidence that the equivalent regression line for all 720 months in the 60-year period has a slope that is not equal to zero. Which of the following is closest to the p-value for this test?

     (A) 0   (B) 0.0178   (C) 0.0089   (D) 0.0356   (E) 0.187

Answer

13. The random variable X is normally distributed with mean 120 and standard deviation 20. Which of the following is equal to $P(110 \leq X \leq 130)$?

     (A) $P(X \leq 110) + P(X \geq 130)$
     (B) $P(X \geq 110) \cdot P(X \leq 130)$
     (C) $P(X \leq 130) - P(X \geq 110)$
     (D) $2 \cdot P(0 \leq X \leq 130)$
     (E) $2 \cdot P(120 \leq X \leq 130)$

Answer

14. The weights of the sheep in a very large population are known to be normally distributed, however the population mean and the population standard deviation are unknown. A random sample of 20 sheep is selected from the population and the weight of each sheep in the sample is measured. The sample values are displayed using a dotplot, and the distribution of the sample values is observed to be roughly symmetrical and to include no outliers.

Following this, a hypothesis test will be performed concerning the mean weight of the population of sheep. What distribution should be used to find the p-value for this test?

(A) A normal distribution should be used because the population is known to be normally distributed.

(B) A normal distribution should be used because the distribution of the sample values is observed to be roughly symmetrical and to include no outliers.

(C) A t-distribution should be used because the sample standard deviation is unknown.

(D) A t-distribution should be used because the population standard deviation is unknown.

(E) A t-distribution should be used because the sample is too small for it to be known that the sampling distribution of the sample mean is normal.

Answer

15. As part of a social game, the Romans would roll an *astragalus*. Suppose that one astragalus has four possible outcomes, which we will name "King," "Steward," "Peasant," and "Thief," respectively. If "Peasant" is four times as likely as "King," "Thief" is four times as likely as "Steward," and "King" and "Steward" are equally likely, which of the following is closest to the probability that one roll of this astragalus results in "Peasant"?

(A) 0.1   (B) 0.2   (C) 0.3   (D) 0.4   (E) 0.5

Answer

16. A company is comparing two types of additive for gasoline: Additive A and Additive B. A random sample of ten brands of car is selected and, under controlled driving conditions, each brand is tested for gasoline mileage (in miles per gallon) with each of the two additives. For each brand of car, the difference (gas mileage with Additive B − gas mileage with Additive A) is calculated.

The distribution of the 10 differences is displayed by means of a boxplot and is found to be roughly symmetrical and to contain no outliers. The mean of the differences is 0.48 and the standard deviation of the differences is 0.766. Which of the following is a 95% confidence interval for the mean difference in gas mileage for the two additives over all brands of car?

(A) $0.48 \pm 1.812 \times \dfrac{0.766}{\sqrt{10}}$

(B) $0.48 \pm 2.228 \times \dfrac{0.766}{\sqrt{9}}$

(C) $0.48 \pm 2.228 \times \dfrac{0.766}{\sqrt{10}}$

(D) $0.48 \pm 2.262 \times \dfrac{0.766}{\sqrt{9}}$

(E) $0.48 \pm 2.262 \times \dfrac{0.766}{\sqrt{10}}$

Answer

17. The weights of the items made by a machine (Machine 1) are normally distributed with standard deviation 2.1 grams and unknown mean, μ_1. The weights of the items made by a second machine (Machine 2) are normally distributed with standard deviation 2.9 grams and unknown mean, μ_2. A random sample of 18 items made by Machine 1 is selected, and the resulting 95% confidence interval for μ_1 is found to be (14.223, 16.164). A random sample (independent of the first random sample) of 20 items made by Machine 2 is selected, and the resulting 95% confidence interval for μ_2 is found to be (16.388, 18.930). Which of the following is the 95% confidence interval for $\mu_2 - \mu_1$ calculated from these two samples?

(A) $(-3.807, -1.123)$
(B) $(1.650, 3.281)$
(C) $(0.867, 4.064)$
(D) $(1.123, 3.807)$
(E) $(2.165, 2.766)$

Answer

18. Suppose that a study has revealed a correlation of -0.898 between the time spent watching TV and verbal ability amongst a large number of kindergarten girls. The study was carried out using verbal test scores and by asking the girls' parents about the girls' TV-watching habits. Which of the following can NOT be concluded about these girls from the information given? (You may assume that the parents have been accurate in their reporting of the girls' TV-watching habits.)

(A) There is a strong linear relationship between the time spent watching TV and the test scores.
(B) Most of the variability in the test scores can be explained by a linear relationship between time spent watching TV and test scores.
(C) Generally a large amount of TV-watching was associated with low test scores.
(D) Generally a small amount of TV-watching was associated with high test scores.
(E) Watching a large amount of TV has caused low test scores.

Answer

19. A company has developed a new chemical designed to prevent sunburn, and is planning an experiment to determine whether the chemical is effective. A lotion has been produced consisting of the chemical in a liquid base, and an intern working for the company suggests the following experimental design:

A set of volunteers will be randomly assigned to two groups: a treatment group and a control group. The experiment will be conducted at a location where there is consistent sunshine. All the experimental subjects will be given identical instructions as to when and how to sunbathe during a one-week period, and will have their skin inspected at the beginning and at the end of that period. In addition, people in the treatment group will be given instructions as to when and how to apply the lotion. People in the control group will be told not to use any protection against the sun.

What useful information might be gained by including a control group in the way described rather than using only a treatment group in the experiment?

(A) If the people in the treatment group seem to have been protected from burning, the results from the control group could give an idea as to whether it was the chemical being tested or just the liquid base that was providing this protection.

(B) If the people in the treatment group seem to have been protected from burning, the results for the control group could enable the experimenters to detect whether this protection came about as a result of the placebo effect.

(C) The result for the control group could give the experimenters information as to whether the combined effects of the chemical, the liquid base, and any possible placebo effect is providing protection against the sun.

(D) The results for the control group could give the experimenters information as to whether the results of the experiment could be generalized to all people who might be exposed to the sun.

(E) The results for the control group could give the experimenters information as to whether the randomization has produced groups that are roughly equal in terms of vulnerability to burning.

Answer

20. It is has been estimated that 20% of the students at a large college own bicycles. In order to determine the accuracy of this estimate a random sample of students from the college is selected. Each student in the sample is asked whether he or she owns a bicycle. Using the data obtained from the sample, a test is conducted of the null hypothesis $H_0: p = 0.2$ against the alternative hypothesis $H_a: p \neq 0.2$, where p is the proportion of all students at the college who own bicycles. Of the following, which is the best interpretation of the p-value for the test?

   (A) The probability that H_0 is true
   (B) The probability that H_a is true
   (C) The probability that H_0 should be rejected
   (D) The probability of getting a sample proportion at least as far from 0.2 as the one obtained, given that H_0 is true
   (E) The probability of getting a sample proportion at least as far from 0.2 as the one obtained, given that H_a is true

Answer
[ ]

21. The distribution of the taxable values of the homes in a large city is observed to be positively skewed. Roughly what percentage of the taxable values will be within two standard deviations of the mean?

   (A) 68
   (B) 95.4
   (C) 97.7
   (D) 99.7
   (E) The percentage cannot be estimated from the information given.

Answer
[ ]

22. A 95% confidence interval is to be constructed to estimate the proportion p of subscribers to a magazine who favor an increase in advertising in return for a lower price. In addition, a hypothesis test (using a 0.05 significance level) concerning the value of p will be performed. Initially, it is thought that the data will be obtained from a simple random sample of 1000 subscribers. Subsequently, use of a simple random sample of 2000 subscribers is considered. Which of the following is NOT likely to result from this increase in the sample size?

(A) A decrease in the width of the confidence interval
(B) A decrease in the probability of a Type I error in the hypothesis test
(C) A decrease in the probability of a Type II error in the hypothesis test
(D) An increase in the power of the hypothesis test
(E) A decrease in the standard deviation of the sampling distribution of the sample proportion

Answer
☐

23. Consider the following three distributions:

- the standard normal distribution (written as "$N(0,1)$")
- the t-distribution with 5 degrees of freedom (written as "t_5")
- the t-distribution with 10 degrees of freedom (written as "t_{10}")

The task here is to list these three distributions according to the values of their standard deviations, giving the distribution with the smallest standard deviation first. Which of the following is the correct list?

(A) $N(0,1), t_5, t_{10}$
(B) $N(0,1), t_{10}, t_5$
(C) $t_5, N(0,1), t_{10}$
(D) $t_5, t_{10}, N(0,1)$
(E) $t_{10}, t_5, N(0,1)$

Answer
☐

24. A government education committee is planning a study of the reading ability of third graders in a large city. The committee intends to use cluster sampling for the study. As part of the planning process, the population of third grade children in the city will be divided into clusters. Of the following, which would be the most suitable criterion for the choice of clusters?

(A) Each cluster should be a simple random sample of third grade children from the city.
(B) Each cluster should as much as possible be representative of third graders in the city as a whole in terms of reading ability.
(C) All the clusters should be different from each other in terms of reading ability.
(D) Each cluster should represent a certain level of third grade reading ability.
(E) There should be as many clusters as possible.

Answer

25. A car dealership sells Sedans, Vans, and SUVs, only. The dealership has a downtown office and a suburban office. The numbers of vehicles in the various categories sold by the dealership during a particular year are shown in the table below.

	Sedans	Vans	SUVs
Downtown Office	977	244	610
Suburban Office	421	361	326

Suppose that a vehicle is chosen at random from the list of all the vehicles sold by the dealership during that year. Let A be the event that the vehicle is a sedan, and let B be the event that the vehicle was bought from the downtown office. Which of the following is true?

(A) The events A and B are independent and mutually exclusive.
(B) The events A and B are independent but not mutually exclusive.
(C) The events A and B are not independent, but they are mutually exclusive.
(D) The events A and B are not independent and are not mutually exclusive.
(E) It is impossible to tell from the information given whether the events A and B are mutually exclusive.

Answer

26. The mean length of a large population of crayfish is μ. A random sample of crayfish will be taken, and then a test will be performed of the null hypothesis $H_0: \mu = 7.5$ against the alternative hypothesis $H_a: \mu > 7.5$, using a significance level of $\alpha = 0.05$. If the true value of μ is actually greater than 7.5, then the power of the test is

   (A) the probability that H_0 is rejected in favor of H_a
   (B) the probability that H_0 is not rejected in favor of H_a
   (C) the probability that H_a is rejected in favor of H_0
   (D) 0.05
   (E) 0.95

   Answer

27. The administration of a large college is considering introducing random drug testing for students at the college. A random sample of 80 male students has been selected, and 23 of them have responded that they approve of random drug testing, with the remaining 57 responding that they do not approve. In addition, a random sample of 100 female students has been selected, and 38 of them have responded that they approve of random drug testing, with the remaining 62 responding that they do not approve. (The two samples were selected independently.) The administration now needs to estimate the proportion of all students at the college who would approve of the policy. Since there are roughly equal numbers of males and females at the college, this could be done by calculating the mean of the two sample proportions:
$$\frac{23/80 + 38/100}{2} = 0.334.$$

   What is the standard error of this estimate?

   (A) $\sqrt{\dfrac{(23/80)(57/80)}{80} + \dfrac{(38/100)(62/100)}{100}}$

   (B) $\sqrt{\dfrac{1}{2}\left(\dfrac{(23/80)(57/80)}{80} + \dfrac{(38/100)(62/100)}{100}\right)}$

   (C) $\dfrac{1}{2}\sqrt{\dfrac{(23/80)(57/80)}{80} + \dfrac{(38/100)(62/100)}{100}}$

   (D) $\sqrt{\dfrac{(23/80)(57/80)}{80} - \dfrac{(38/100)(62/100)}{100}}$

   (E) $\sqrt{\dfrac{1}{2}\left(\dfrac{(23/80)(57/80)}{80} - \dfrac{(38/100)(62/100)}{100}\right)}$

   Answer

28. An experiment is being designed to compare the effectiveness of two types of fertilizer. Seeds of a single species of plant will be used in the experiment. The site for the experiment is a rectangular field that is positioned symmetrically between two rivers. One of the rivers is to the west of the field and the other is to the east. The field has been divided into twelve plots of approximately the same area, and the plots are numbered 1 through 12 as shown in the diagram. It is understood that the closer a plot is to a river, the more water it will receive, and the further a plot is to the south, the more light it will receive.

The designers of the experiment have decided that the plots should be blocked. Within each block, the fertilizers will be randomly assigned to equal numbers of plots.

We use the notation {1, 2, 3}, for example, to mean that plots 1, 2, and 3 form a block. Of the following blocking schemes, which is the most suitable for this experiment?

(A) {1, 3, 5, 7, 9, 11} {2, 4, 6, 8, 10, 12}
(B) {1, 2, 5, 6, 9, 10} {3, 4, 7, 8, 11, 12}
(C) {1, 2, 3, 4} {5, 6, 7, 8} {9, 10, 11, 12}
(D) {1, 5, 9} {2, 6, 10} {3, 7, 11} {4, 8, 12}
(E) {1, 4} {2, 3} {5, 8} {6, 7} {9, 12} {10, 11}

Answer

29. A random sample of size 20 is taken from a large population of horses. The heights of the horses in the sample are measured in centimeters. Using a t-distribution, the resulting 95% confidence interval for the population mean height, μ, is found to be (158.28, 160.92). Which of the following conclusions can be deduced from the information given?

(A) We have convincing evidence at the 5% level that $\mu = 158.4$.
(B) We have convincing evidence at the 5% level that $\mu \neq 158.4$.
(C) We have convincing evidence at the 2.5% level that $\mu \neq 158.4$.
(D) We do not have convincing evidence at the 5% level that $\mu \neq 158.4$.
(E) We do not have convincing evidence at the 5% level that $\mu > 158.4$.

Answer

30. An employee working at a lost-and-found office in a large railroad station is interested in the designs of umbrellas. For a sequence of 300 umbrellas that pass through the office, he notes for each its color (with categories "black," "single non-black color," and "at least two colors") and its type (with categories "telescopic" and "non-telescopic"). He compiles the results in a table, some of which is shown below. (Some of the numbers have been replaced by asterisks.)

	Telescopic	Non-Telescopic	Total
Black	*	59	*
Single non-Black Color	47	*	79
At Least Two Colors	13	*	35
Total	*	*	300

We can consider the set of 300 umbrellas to be a random sample of umbrellas that pass through the office. If color is independent of type, which of the following is closest to the expected number of black telescopic umbrellas?

(A) 70.0   (B) 78.7   (C) 79.2   (D) 115.9   (E) 127.7

Answer

31. In a large country, the distribution of the heights of married men is normal with mean 68.9 inches and standard deviation 2.9 inches. The distribution of the heights of married women is normal with mean 63.8 inches and standard deviation 2.5 inches.

   A married couple is to be chosen at random. Let the random variable Z be the sum of the height of the man and the height of the woman.

   Which of the following statements can be concluded from the information given?

   I. $\mu_Z = 68.9 + 63.8$

   II. $\sigma_Z = \sqrt{2.9^2 + 2.5^2}$

   III. The distribution of Z is normal.

   (A) I only
   (B) III only
   (C) I and II only
   (D) I, II, and III
   (E) None of the statements can be concluded from the information given.

Answer

32. A random sample of size 15 is taken from a population that is known to be normally distributed. The population mean and the population standard deviation are both unknown. The sample values are displayed in the dotplot below, along with a dotted line representing the sample mean. (Note that one point cannot be seen as it is very close to another point.)

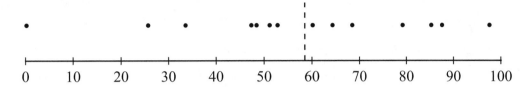

A 95% confidence interval for the population mean is calculated using the sample values. Which of the following could represent that confidence interval?

(A)

(B)

(C)

(D)

(E)

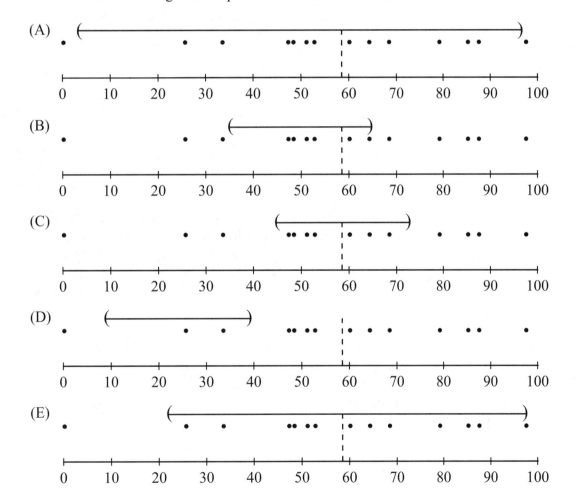

Answer

33. A data set with mean 52.3 and standard deviation 10.8 is to be transformed to a new data set using one of the transformations below, where x represents a value in the original data set and y represents its corresponding value in the new data set. If the new data set is to have mean 80.6 and standard deviation 7.9, which of the transformations is correct?

(A) $y = \dfrac{10.8}{7.9}x + 28.3$

(B) $y = \dfrac{10.8}{7.9}(x - 52.3) + 80.6$

(C) $y = \dfrac{7.9}{10.8}(x + 28.3)$

(D) $y = \dfrac{7.9}{10.8}x + 28.3$

(E) $y = \dfrac{7.9}{10.8}(x - 52.3) + 80.6$

Answer

34. A random sample of organisms from a particular species is obtained, and the number of males and the number of females in the sample are counted. A biologist wishes to investigate whether the data obtained provide convincing evidence that the proportion of males in the species as a whole is different from 0.5. The biologist uses a one-proportion z-test for this purpose. Which of the following inference procedures could also be used to investigate the biologist's question? (You may assume that the conditions for inference are met.)

(A) Two-sample t-test for the difference of two means
(B) Paired t-test for the difference of two means
(C) Two-sample z-test for the difference of two proportions
(D) Chi-square test for goodness of fit
(E) Chi-square test for homogeneity

Answer

35. A company employs a total of 810 people, consisting of 500 manual workers, 280 clerical workers, and 30 managerial staff. An investigator intends to conduct a survey using a sample of the company's employees. Using the company's computer records, the investigator will randomly select 50 manual workers, 28 clerical workers, and 3 managerial staff. Will the sample obtained in this way be a simple random sample of the company's employees?

(A) Yes, because every employee has an equal probability of being included in the sample.
(B) Yes, because every set of 81 employees has an equal chance of being the sample.
(C) No, because not every employee has an equal probability of being included in the sample.
(D) No, because not every set of 81 employees has an equal chance of being the sample.
(E) It is impossible to tell from the information given whether or not this will be a simple random sample of employees.

Answer

36. The standard deviation of the lifetime of a particular brand of car battery is 4.3 months. A random sample of 10 of these batteries is taken. Assuming that the lifetimes of all batteries of this brand are normally distributed, what is the probability that the mean lifetime for this sample is within 1 month of the mean lifetime for all batteries of this brand?

(A) 0.019   (B) 0.184   (C) 0.519   (D) 0.538   (E) 0.769

Answer

37.

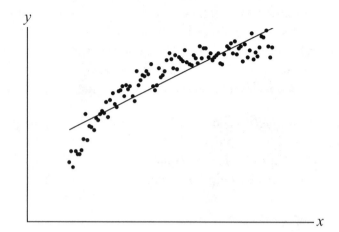

The scatterplot for a particular data set is shown above. The least squares regression line has been added. Which of the following could be the residual plot for this data set?

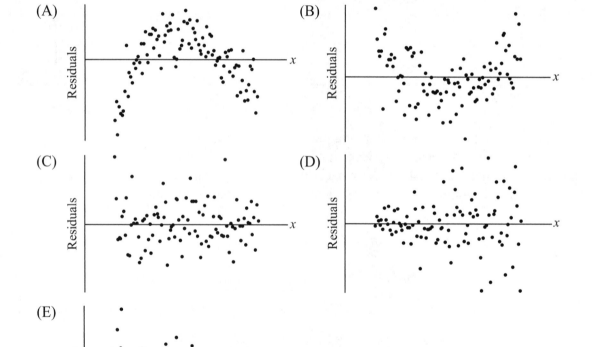

Answer

38. Drew goes to a magic store and buys a coin called "Jerry's Weighted Coin." He flips the coin 200 times and 107 of the flips result in "heads." Denoting the proportion of all flips of this coin that result in "heads" by p, which of the following can be deduced from this result?

    (A) $p = 0.535$.
    (B) $p = 0.5$.
    (C) We are 95% confident that p is between 0.466 and 0.604.
    (D) If the procedure of flipping the coin 200 times were to be repeated a large number of times, then on 95% of occasions the proportion of the 200 flips that are "heads" would be between 0.466 and 0.604.
    (E) If the coin were to be flipped a further 200 times, we are 95% confident that the proportion of flips that are "heads" would be between 0.466 and 0.604.

Answer

39.

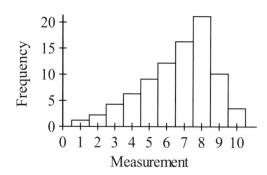

A set of measurements takes whole number values between 1 and 10 inclusive, and has the histogram shown above. Which of the following is the cumulative relative frequency graph for the same data set?

(A)

(B)

(C)

(D)

(E)

Answer

40. A bag contains 5 red beads, 3 green beads, and 2 blue beads. If three beads are picked from the bag at random (without replacement), what is the probability that the beads that are picked are all different colors?

(A) $\left(\dfrac{5}{10}\right)\left(\dfrac{3}{10}\right)\left(\dfrac{2}{10}\right)$

(B) $3\left(\dfrac{5}{10}\right)\left(\dfrac{3}{10}\right)\left(\dfrac{2}{10}\right)$

(C) $\left(\dfrac{5}{10}\right)\left(\dfrac{3}{9}\right)\left(\dfrac{2}{8}\right)$

(D) $3\left(\dfrac{5}{10}\right)\left(\dfrac{3}{9}\right)\left(\dfrac{2}{8}\right)$

(E) $6\left(\dfrac{5}{10}\right)\left(\dfrac{3}{9}\right)\left(\dfrac{2}{8}\right)$

Answer

SECTION II
Part A
Questions 1–5
Spend about 65 minutes on this part of the exam.
Percent of Section II grade—75

Directions: Show all your work. Indicate clearly the methods you use, because you will be graded on the correctness of your method as well as on the accuracy and completeness of your results and explanations.

1. A factory has been in operation since 1952, and has had trouble with system breakdowns since then. The company that owns the factory has kept note of the number of breakdowns occurring each year. The factory was refurbished in January 1979, and it is thought that possibly the problem with breakdowns was less severe between then and 2008 than it had been previously.

   The data below are the number of breakdowns that occurred each year, first from 1952 to 1978, and second from 1979 to 2008.

   1952-1978: 4 3 2 2 4 0 1 1 5 3 2 5 3 5 2 4 1 5 2 6 3 3 2 4 3 0 2
   1979-2008: 0 3 0 1 2 2 3 3 2 1 3 3 2 1 1 6 2 4 2 1 2 3 2 1 5 1 2 3 2 2

   (a) Complete the frequency table below.

Number of Breakdowns	Frequency 1952-1978	Frequency 1979-2008
0	2	
1	3	
2		
3		
4		
5		
6		

(b) Display these data graphically so that the distributions of the annual numbers of breakdowns during these two time periods can easily be compared.

(c) Based on an examination of your graphical display, comment on whether the occurrence of breakdowns seems to have been less after January 1979. (No calculations are necessary.)

(d) Briefly, how would you describe the shape of the distribution of annual numbers of breakdowns in the years 1952 to 1978, and how would you describe the shape of the distribution of annual numbers of breakdowns in the years 1979 to 2008?

2. The students at a high school are split roughly equally across grades 9 through 12. A group of students in a statistics class at the school wishes to estimate the mean time spent studying by students at the school during the previous seven days. The group decides to select a sample of 40 students from the school, to ask those students how many hours they have studied during the previous seven days, and to use the mean value for the sample as an estimate of the mean value for the school.

(a) One of the students in the group thinks that they should use a simple random sample. Describe how this sample might be selected.

A different student thinks that they should use stratified random sampling, with the strata being the grades (9 through 12). (The sample size will again be 40.)

(b) How might this stratified sample be selected?

(c) What is it about the grade levels (9 through 12) that might make them suitable to be used as strata in this study?

(d) Why might it be preferable to use the stratified sampling described, rather than a simple random sample?

3. Consider two games at a village fair, Game A and Game B. Let the gain in dollars in one play of Game A be denoted by the random variable X, and let the gain in dollars in one play of Game B be denoted by the random variable Y. (A negative gain means that you receive less money back from the game than you paid to take part.)

The probability distributions of X and Y are given below.

X	−5	−2	1	4	10
Probability	0.33	0.27	0.20	0.13	0.07

Y	−5	−2	1	4	25
Probability	0.37	0.32	0.16	0.10	0.05

You may assume that the result of any play of either of the games is independent of the result of any other play of either of the games.

(a) In any one play of Game A, what is the probability that your gain will be positive? In any one play of Game B, what is the probability that your gain will be positive?

(b) The expected value and the standard deviation of the money gained in one play of Game A are $-\$0.77$ and $\$4.24$, respectively. Calculate the expected value and the standard deviation of the money gained in one play of Game B.

(c) Suppose that you are considering making a large number of plays of Game A, or making a large number of plays of Game B, and you want to decide which of these is the more sensible financially. A friend tells you that, since your gain is more likely to be positive in any one play of Game A than it is in any one play of Game B, Game A should be your choice. Is this a correct argument? Explain why or why not.

4. A car rental company is conducting a study regarding the types of car preferred by customers at the company's various locations. The table below summarizes the reservations over a seven-day period at three of the company's locations.

	Type				Total
	Compact	Standard	Full Size	Other	
Location 1	76	75	40	59	250
Location 2	90	78	47	62	277
Location 3	96	64	61	51	272

The company is willing to consider the 250 reservations at Location 1 as a random sample from the set of all reservations at Location 1, the 277 reservations at Location 2 as a random sample from the set of all reservations at Location 2, and the 272 reservations at Location 3 as a random sample from the set of all reservations at Location 3. Do these data provide sufficient evidence to indicate a difference in the distributions of the car types between the populations of reservations at the three locations? Provide statistical evidence to support your conclusion.

5. The 28 students in a fourth-grade class were taken to a rocky beach. The students were all given identical metal containers and were asked to collect as many pebbles as they wished. Once the activity was over, the teacher recorded, for each student, the number of pebbles collected (x) and the weight (y), to the nearest ounce, of the filled container. The results are shown in the scatterplot below. Only 26 of the 28 pairs are visible because some of the (x, y) pairs were the same. The equation of the least squares regression line is $\hat{y} = 13.419 + 3.865x$.

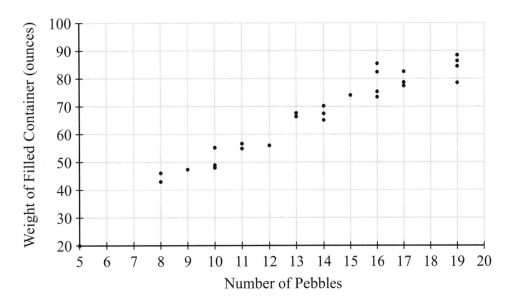

(a) Draw the least squares regression line on the scatterplot. (Note that the smallest value on the horizontal axis is 5, not 0.)

(b) One student collected 16 pebbles, and the weight of the filled container for this student was 82 ounces. Circle the point on the scatterplot that represents this student's results and draw the line segment on the scatterplot that corresponds to the residual for this point. Give a numerical value of this residual.

(c) In the context of this question, interpret the value of the residual you found in part (b).

(d) Do the values of the slope and the intercept of the least squares regression line have meaningful interpretations in the context of this question? If so, provide interpretations in this context. If not, explain why not.

SECTION II
Part B
Question 6
Spend about 25 minutes on this part of the exam.
Percent of Section II grade—25

Directions: Show all your work. Indicate clearly the methods you use, because you will be graded on the correctness of your method as well as on the accuracy and completeness of your results and explanations.

6. A company that manufactures exercise equipment for use in the home is considering a new marketing approach in which people who attend public gyms are specifically targeted. It has been thought for several years that roughly 60% of people who attend public gyms have exercise equipment at home. In order to gather some data to investigate the truth of this, the company sends an employee, Amy, to a downtown gym in the city in which the company is based.

   Amy speaks to 83 of the gym's members as they leave the building, and asks each person whether he/she has exercise equipment at home. Of these 83 people, 42 reply that they have exercise equipment at home, and the remaining 41 reply that they do not.

   We can assume that the 83 people in Amy's sample form a random sample of the gym's members, and that the gym has a large number of members.

   (a) Use a one-proportion z-test to determine whether this result provides convincing evidence that fewer than 60% of the gym's members have exercise equipment at home.

If you need more room for your work for part (a), use the space below.

The company sends a second employee, Leonard, to a more exclusive suburban gym. Using the same method as Amy, Leonard finds that in a sample of 10 of the suburban gym's members, 2 respond that they have exercise equipment at home, and the remaining 8 respond that they do not. We can assume that the 10 people in Leonard's sample form a random sample of the suburban gym's members, and that the gym has a large number of members.

(b) Explain why a one-proportion z-test cannot be used to determine whether Leonard's result provides convincing evidence that fewer than 60% of the suburban gym's members have exercise equipment at home.

(c) Suppose that exactly 60% of the suburban gym's members have exercise equipment at home. What is the probability that, in a random sample of 10 of the gym's members, 2 or fewer will have exercise equipment at home?

(d) Does your answer to (c), along with the result of Leonard's survey, lead you to suspect that fewer than 60% of the suburban gym's members have exercise equipment at home? Explain your reasoning.

Formulas and Tables

(I) Descriptive Statistics

$$\bar{x} = \frac{\sum x_i}{n}$$

$$s_x = \sqrt{\frac{1}{n-1} \sum (x_i - \bar{x})^2}$$

$$s_p = \sqrt{\frac{(n_1 - 1)s_1^2 + (n_2 - 1)s_2^2}{(n_1 - 1) + (n_2 - 1)}}$$

$$\hat{y} = b_0 + b_1 x$$

$$b_1 = \frac{\sum (x_i - \bar{x})(y_i - \bar{y})}{\sum (x_i - \bar{x})^2}$$

$$b_0 = \bar{y} - b_1 \bar{x}$$

$$r = \frac{1}{n-1} \sum \left(\frac{x_i - \bar{x}}{s_x} \right) \left(\frac{y_i - \bar{y}}{s_y} \right)$$

$$b_1 = r \frac{s_y}{s_x}$$

$$s_{b_1} = \frac{\sqrt{\dfrac{\sum (y_i - \hat{y}_i)^2}{n-2}}}{\sqrt{\sum (x_i - \bar{x})^2}}$$

256

(II) Probability

$$P(A \cup B) = P(A) + P(B) - P(A \cap B)$$

$$P(A \mid B) = \frac{P(A \cap B)}{P(B)}$$

$$E(X) = \mu_x = \sum x_i p_i$$

$$\mathrm{Var}(X) = \sigma_x^2 = \sum (x_i - \mu_x)^2 p_i$$

If X has a binomial distribution with parameters n and p, then:

$$P(X = k) = \binom{n}{k} p^k (1 - p)^{n-k}$$

$$\mu_x = np$$

$$\sigma_x = \sqrt{np(1 - p)}$$

$$\mu_{\hat{p}} = p$$

$$\sigma_{\hat{p}} = \sqrt{\frac{p(1 - p)}{n}}$$

If $\overline{x}$ is the mean of a random sample of size n from an infinite population with mean μ and standard deviation σ, then:

$$\mu_{\overline{x}} = \mu$$

$$\sigma_{\overline{x}} = \frac{\sigma}{\sqrt{n}}$$

(III)   Inferential Statistics

Standardized test statistic: $\dfrac{\text{statistic} - \text{parameter}}{\text{standard deviation of statistic}}$

Confidence interval: $\text{statistic} \pm (\text{critical value}) \cdot (\text{standard deviation of statistic})$

Single-Sample

Statistic	Standard Deviation of Statistic
Sample Mean	$\dfrac{\sigma}{\sqrt{n}}$
Sample Proportion	$\sqrt{\dfrac{p(1-p)}{n}}$

Two-Sample

Statistic	Standard Deviation of Statistic
Difference of sample means	$\sqrt{\dfrac{\sigma_1^2}{n_1} + \dfrac{\sigma_2^2}{n_2}}$ Special case when $\sigma_1 = \sigma_2$ $\sigma\sqrt{\dfrac{1}{n_1} + \dfrac{1}{n_2}}$
Difference of sample proportions	$\sqrt{\dfrac{p_1(1-p_1)}{n_1} + \dfrac{p_2(1-p_2)}{n_2}}$ Special case when $p_1 = p_2$ $\sqrt{p(1-p)}\sqrt{\dfrac{1}{n_1} + \dfrac{1}{n_2}}$

$$\text{Chi-square test statistic} = \sum \dfrac{(\text{observed} - \text{expected})^2}{\text{expected}}$$

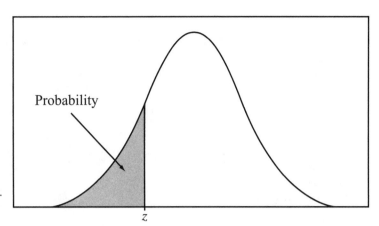

Table entry for z is the
probability lying below z.

Table A Standard normal probabilities

z	.00	.01	.02	.03	.04	.05	.06	.07	.08	.09
− 3.4	.0003	.0003	.0003	.0003	.0003	.0003	.0003	.0003	.0003	.0002
− 3.3	.0005	.0005	.0005	.0004	.0004	.0004	.0004	.0004	.0004	.0003
− 3.2	.0007	.0007	.0006	.0006	.0006	.0006	.0006	.0005	.0005	.0005
− 3.1	.0010	.0009	.0009	.0009	.0008	.0008	.0008	.0008	.0007	.0007
− 3.0	.0013	.0013	.0013	.0012	.0012	.0011	.0011	.0011	.0010	.0010
− 2.9	.0019	.0018	.0018	.0017	.0016	.0016	.0015	.0015	.0014	.0014
− 2.8	.0026	.0025	.0024	.0023	.0023	.0022	.0021	.0021	.0020	.0019
− 2.7	.0035	.0034	.0033	.0032	.0031	.0030	.0029	.0028	.0027	.0026
− 2.6	.0047	.0045	.0044	.0043	.0041	.0040	.0039	.0038	.0037	.0036
− 2.5	.0062	.0060	.0059	.0057	.0055	.0054	.0052	.0051	.0049	.0048
− 2.4	.0082	.0080	.0078	.0075	.0073	.0071	.0069	.0068	.0066	.0064
− 2.3	.0107	.0104	.0102	.0099	.0096	.0094	.0091	.0089	.0087	.0084
− 2.2	.0139	.0136	.0132	.0129	.0125	.0122	.0119	.0116	.0113	.0110
− 2.1	.0179	.0174	.0170	.0166	.0162	.0158	.0154	.0150	.0146	.0143
− 2.0	.0228	.0222	.0217	.0212	.0207	.0202	.0197	.0192	.0188	.0183
− 1.9	.0287	.0281	.0274	.0268	.0262	.0256	.0250	.0244	.0239	.0233
− 1.8	.0359	.0351	.0344	.0336	.0329	.0322	.0314	.0307	.0301	.0294
− 1.7	.0446	.0436	.0427	.0418	.0409	.0401	.0392	.0384	.0375	.0367
− 1.6	.0548	.0537	.0526	.0516	.0505	.0495	.0485	.0475	.0465	.0455
− 1.5	.0668	.0655	.0634	.0630	.0618	.0606	.0594	.0582	.0571	.0559
− 1.4	.0808	.0793	.0778	.0764	.0749	.0735	.0721	.0708	.0694	.0681
− 1.3	.0968	.0951	.0934	.0918	.0901	.0885	.0869	.0853	.0838	.0823
− 1.2	.1151	.1131	.1112	.1093	.1075	.1056	.1038	.1020	.1003	.0985
− 1.1	.1357	.1335	.1314	.1292	.1271	.1251	.1230	.1210	.1190	.1170
− 1.0	.1587	.1562	.1539	.1515	.1492	.1469	.1446	.1423	.1401	.1379
− 0.9	.1841	.1814	.1778	.1762	.1736	.1711	.1685	.1660	.1635	.1611
− 0.8	.2119	.2090	.2061	.2033	.2005	.1977	.1949	.1922	.1894	.1867
− 0.7	.2420	.2389	.2358	.2327	.2296	.2266	.2236	.2206	.2177	.2148
− 0.6	.2743	.2709	.2676	.2643	.2611	.2578	.2546	.2514	.2483	.2451
− 0.5	.3085	.3050	.3015	.2981	.2946	.2912	.2877	.2843	.2810	.2776
− 0.4	.3446	.3409	.3372	.3336	.3300	.3264	.3228	.3192	.3156	.3121
− 0.3	.3821	.3783	.3745	.3707	.3669	.3632	.3594	.3557	.3520	.3483
− 0.2	.4207	.4168	.4129	.4090	.4052	.4013	.3974	.3936	.3897	.3859
− 0.1	.4602	.4562	.4522	.4483	.4443	.4404	.4364	.4325	.4286	.4247
− 0.0	.5000	.4960	.4920	.4880	.4840	.4801	.4761	.4721	.4681	.4641

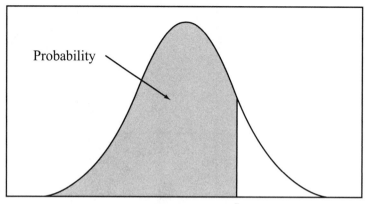

Table entry for z is the
probability lying below z.

Table A   (*Continued*)

z	.00	.01	.02	.03	.04	.05	.06	.07	.08	.09
0.0	.5000	.5040	.5080	.5120	.5160	.5199	.5239	.5279	.5319	.5359
0.1	.5398	.5438	.5478	.5517	.5557	.5596	.5636	.5675	.5714	.5753
0.2	.5793	.5832	.5871	.5910	.5948	.5987	.6026	.6064	.6103	.6141
0.3	.6179	.6217	.6255	.6293	.6331	.6368	.6406	.6443	.6480	.6517
0.4	.6554	.6591	.6628	.6664	.6700	.6736	.6772	.6808	.6844	.6879
0.5	.6915	.6950	.6985	.7019	.7054	.7088	.7123	.7157	.7190	.7224
0.6	.7257	.7291	.7324	.7357	.7389	.7422	.7454	.7486	.7517	.7549
0.7	.7580	.7611	.7642	.7673	.7704	.7734	.7764	.7794	.7823	.7852
0.8	.7881	.7910	.7939	.7967	.7995	.8023	.8051	.8078	.8106	.8133
0.9	.8159	.8186	.8212	.8238	.8264	.8289	.8315	.8340	.8365	.8389
1.0	.8413	.8438	.8461	.8485	.8508	.8531	.8554	.8577	.8599	.8621
1.1	.8643	.8665	.8686	.8708	.8729	.8749	.8770	.8790	.8810	.8830
1.2	.8849	.8869	.8888	.8907	.8925	.8944	.8962	.8980	.8997	.9015
1.3	.9032	.9049	.9066	.9082	.9099	.9115	.9131	.9147	.9162	.9177
1.4	.9192	.9207	.9222	.9236	.9251	.9265	.9279	.9292	.9306	.9319
1.5	.9332	.9345	.9357	.9370	.9382	.9394	.9406	.9418	.9429	.9441
1.6	.9452	.9436	.9474	.9484	.9495	.9505	.9515	.9525	.9535	.9545
1.7	.9554	.9564	.9537	.9582	.9591	.9599	.9608	.9616	.9625	.9633
1.8	.9641	.9649	.9656	.9664	.9671	.9678	.9686	.9693	.9699	.9706
1.9	.9713	.9719	.9726	.9732	.9738	.9744	.9750	.9756	.9761	.9767
2.0	.9772	.9778	.9783	.9788	.9793	.9798	.9803	.9808	.9812	.9817
2.1	.9821	.9826	.9830	.9834	.9838	.9842	.9846	.9850	.9854	.9857
2.2	.9861	.9864	.9868	.9871	.9875	.9878	.9881	.9884	.9887	.9890
2.3	.9893	.9896	.9898	.9901	.9904	.9906	.9909	.9911	.9913	.9916
2.4	.9918	.9920	.9922	.9925	.9927	.9929	.9931	.9932	.9934	.9936
2.5	.9938	.9940	.9941	.9943	.9945	.9946	.9948	.9949	.9951	.9952
2.6	.9953	.9955	.9956	.9957	.9959	.9960	.9961	.9962	.9963	.9964
2.7	.9965	.9966	.9967	.9968	.9969	.9970	.9971	.9972	.9973	.9974
2.8	.9974	.9975	.9976	.9977	.9977	.9978	.9979	.9979	.9980	.9981
2.9	.9981	.9982	.9982	.9983	.9984	.9984	.9985	.9985	.9986	.9986
3.0	.9987	.9987	.9987	.9988	.9988	.9989	.9989	.9989	.9990	.9990
3.1	.9990	.9991	.9991	.9991	.9992	.9992	.9992	.9992	.9993	.9993
3.2	.9993	.9993	.9994	.9994	.9994	.9994	.9994	.9995	.9995	.9995
3.3	.9995	.9995	.9995	.9996	.9996	.9996	.9996	.9996	.9996	.9997
3.4	.9997	.9997	.9997	.9997	.9997	.9997	.9997	.9997	.9997	.9998

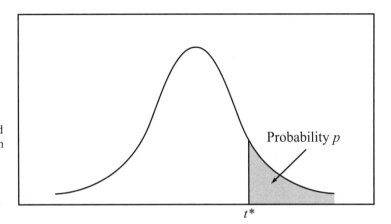

Table entry for p and C is the point t^* with probability p lying above it and probability C lying between $-t^*$ and t^*.

Probability p

t^*

Table B t distribution critical values

df	\multicolumn{12}{c}{Tail probability p}
	.25	.20	.15	.10	.05	.025	.02	.01	.005	.0025	.001	.0005
1	1.000	1.376	1.963	3.078	6.314	12.71	15.89	31.82	63.66	127.3	318.3	636.6
2	.816	1.061	1.386	1.886	2.920	4.303	4.849	6.965	9.925	14.09	22.33	31.60
3	.765	.978	1.250	1.638	2.353	3.182	3.482	4.541	5.841	7.453	10.21	12.92
4	.741	.941	1.190	1.533	2.132	2.776	2.999	3.747	4.604	5.598	7.173	8.610
5	.727	.920	1.156	1.476	2.015	2.571	2.757	3.365	4.032	4.773	5.893	6.869
6	.718	.906	1.134	1.440	1.943	2.447	2.612	3.143	3.707	4.317	5.208	5.959
7	.711	.896	1.119	1.415	1.895	2.365	2.517	2.998	3.499	4.029	4.785	5.408
8	.706	.889	1.108	1.397	1.860	2.306	2.449	2.896	3.355	3.833	4.501	5.041
9	.703	.883	1.100	1.383	1.833	2.262	2.398	2.821	3.250	3.690	4.297	4.781
10	.700	.879	1.093	1.372	1.812	2.228	2.359	2.764	3.169	3.581	4.144	4.587
11	.697	.876	1.088	1.363	1.796	2.201	2.328	2.718	3.106	3.497	4.025	4.437
12	.695	.873	1.083	1.356	1.782	2.179	2.303	2.681	3.055	3.428	3.930	4.318
13	.694	.870	1.079	1.350	1.771	2.160	2.282	2.650	3.012	3.372	3.852	4.221
14	.692	.868	1.076	1.345	1.761	2.145	2.264	2.624	2.977	3.326	3.787	4.140
15	.691	.866	1.074	1.341	1.753	2.131	2.249	2.602	2.947	3.286	3.733	4.073
16	.690	.865	1.071	1.337	1.746	2.120	2.235	2.583	2.921	3.252	3.686	4.015
17	.689	.863	1.069	1.333	1.740	2.110	2.224	2.567	2.898	3.222	3.646	3.965
18	.688	.862	1.067	1.330	1.734	2.101	2.214	2.552	2.878	3.197	3.611	3.922
19	.688	.861	1.066	1.328	1.729	2.093	2.205	2.539	2.861	3.174	3.579	3.883
20	.687	.860	1.064	1.325	1.725	2.086	2.197	2.528	2.845	3.153	3.552	3.850
21	.686	.859	1.063	1.323	1.721	2.080	2.189	2.518	2.831	3.135	3.527	3.819
22	.686	.858	1.061	1.321	1.717	2.074	2.183	2.508	2.819	3.119	3.505	3.792
23	.685	.858	1.060	1.319	1.714	2.069	2.177	2.500	2.807	3.104	3.485	3.768
24	.685	.857	1.059	1.318	1.711	2.064	2.172	2.492	2.797	3.091	3.467	3.745
25	.684	.856	1.058	1.316	1.708	2.060	2.167	2.485	2.787	3.078	3.450	3.725
26	.684	.856	1.058	1.315	1.706	2.056	2.162	2.479	2.779	3.067	3.435	3.707
27	.684	.855	1.057	1.314	1.703	2.052	2.158	2.473	2.771	3.057	3.421	3.690
28	.683	.855	1.056	1.313	1.701	2.048	2.154	2.467	2.763	3.047	3.408	3.674
29	.683	.854	1.055	1.311	1.699	2.045	2.150	2.462	2.756	3.038	3.396	3.659
30	.683	.854	1.055	1.310	1.697	2.042	2.147	2.457	2.750	3.030	3.385	3.646
40	681	.851	1.050	1.303	1.684	2.021	2.123	2.423	2.704	2.971	3.307	3.551
50	.679	.849	1.047	1.299	1.676	2.009	2.109	2.403	2.678	2.937	3.261	3.496
60	.679	.848	1.045	1.296	1.671	2.000	2.099	2.390	2.660	2.915	3.232	3.460
80	.678	.846	1.043	1.292	1.664	1.990	2.088	2.374	2.639	2.887	3.195	3.416
100	.677	.845	1.042	1.290	1.660	1.984	2.081	2.364	2.626	2.871	3.174	3.390
1000	.675	.842	1.037	1.282	1.646	1.962	2.056	2.330	2.581	2.813	3.098	3.300
∞	.674	.841	1.036	1.282	1.645	1.960	2.054	2.326	2.576	2.807	3.091	3.291
	50%	60%	70%	80%	90%	95%	96%	98%	99%	99.5%	99.8%	99.9%
	\multicolumn{12}{c}{Confidence Level C}

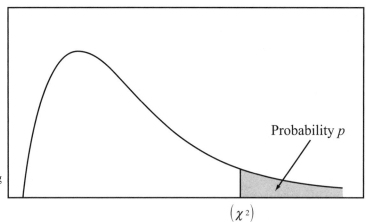

Table entry for p is the point (χ^2) with the probability p lying above it.

Probability p

(χ^2)

Table C χ^2 **critical values**

df	.25	.20	.15	.10	.05	.025	.02	.01	.005	.0025	.001	.0005
					Tail probability p							
1	1.32	1.64	2.07	2.71	3.84	5.02	5.41	6.63	7.88	9.14	10.83	12.12
2	2.77	3.22	3.79	4.61	5.99	7.38	7.82	9.21	10.60	11.98	13.82	15.20
3	4.11	4.64	5.32	6.25	7.81	9.35	9.84	11.34	12.84	14.32	16.27	17.73
4	5.39	5.99	6.74	7.78	9.49	11.14	11.67	13.28	14.86	16.42	18.47	20.00
5	6.63	7.29	8.12	9.24	11.07	12.83	13.39	15.09	16.75	18.39	20.51	22.11
6	7.84	8.56	9.45	10.64	12.59	14.45	15.03	16.81	18.55	20.25	22.46	24.10
7	9.04	9.80	10.75	12.02	14.07	16.01	16.62	18.48	20.28	22.04	24.32	26.02
8	10.22	11.03	12.03	13.36	15.51	17.53	18.17	20.09	21.95	23.77	26.12	27.87
9	11.39	12.24	13.29	14.68	16.92	19.02	19.68	21.67	23.59	25.46	27.88	29.67
10	12.55	13.44	14.53	15.99	18.31	20.48	21.16	23.21	25.19	27.11	29.59	31.42
11	13.70	14.63	15.77	17.28	19.68	21.92	22.62	24.72	26.76	28.73	31.26	33.14
12	14.85	15.81	16.99	18.55	21.03	23.34	24.05	26.22	28.30	30.32	32.91	34.82
13	15.98	16.98	18.20	19.81	22.36	24.74	25.47	27.69	29.82	31.88	34.53	36.48
14	17.12	18.15	19.41	21.06	23.68	26.12	26.87	29.14	31.32	33.43	36.12	38.11
15	18.25	19.31	20.60	22.31	25.00	27.49	28.26	30.58	32.80	34.95	37.70	39.72
16	19.37	20.47	21.79	23.54	26.30	28.85	29.63	32.00	34.27	36.46	39.25	41.31
17	20.49	21.61	22.98	24.77	27.59	30.19	31.00	33.41	35.72	37.95	40.79	42.88
18	21.60	22.76	24.16	25.99	28.87	31.53	32.35	34.81	37.16	39.42	42.31	44.43
19	22.72	23.90	25.33	27.20	30.14	32.85	33.69	36.19	38.58	40.88	43.82	45.97
20	23.83	25.04	26.50	28.41	31.41	34.17	35.02	37.57	40.00	42.34	45.31	47.50
21	24.93	26.17	27.66	29.62	32.67	35.48	36.34	38.93	41.40	43.78	46.80	49.01
22	26.04	27.30	28.82	30.81	33.92	36.78	37.66	40.29	42.80	45.20	48.27	50.51
23	27.14	28.43	29.98	32.01	35.17	38.08	38.97	41.64	44.18	46.62	49.73	52.00
24	28.24	29.55	31.13	33.20	36.42	39.36	40.27	42.98	45.56	48.03	51.18	53.48
25	29.34	30.68	32.28	34.38	37.65	40.65	41.57	44.31	46.93	49.44	52.62	54.95
26	30.43	31.79	33.43	35.56	38.89	41.92	42.86	45.64	48.29	50.83	54.05	56.41
27	31.53	32.91	34.57	36.74	40.11	43.19	44.14	46.96	49.64	52.22	55.48	57.86
28	32.62	34.03	35.71	37.92	41.34	44.46	45.42	48.28	50.99	53.59	56.89	59.30
29	33.71	35.14	36.85	39.09	42.56	45.72	46.69	49.59	52.34	54.97	58.30	60.73
30	34.80	36.25	37.99	40.26	43.77	46.98	47.96	50.89	53.67	56.33	59.70	62.16
40	45.62	47.27	49.24	51.81	55.76	59.34	60.44	63.69	66.77	69.70	73.40	76.09
50	56.33	58.16	60.35	63.17	67.50	71.42	72.61	76.15	79.49	82.66	86.66	89.56
60	66.98	68.97	71.34	74.40	79.08	83.30	84.58	88.38	91.95	95.34	99.61	102.7
80	88.13	90.41	93.11	96.58	101.9	106.6	108.1	112.3	116.3	120.1	124.8	128.3
100	109.1	111.7	114.7	118.5	124.3	129.6	131.1	135.8	140.2	144.3	149.4	153.2

*Roman numerals in **bold** face type represent sample exam numbers. Other numbers are question numbers.*